RECENT HISTORY OF AN ETHIOPIAN DELTA

The Omo River and the level of Lake Rudolf

Karl W. Butzer

The University of Chicago

Cartography by John A. Kirchner

THE UNIVERSITY OF CHICAGO
DEPARTMENT OF GEOGRAPHY
RESEARCH PAPER NO. 136

1971

Library of Congress Catalog Card Number: 70-184080

Research Papers are available from:
The University of Chicago
Department of Geography
5828 S. University Avenue
Chicago, Illinois 60637
Price: $4.50 list; $4.00 series subscription

TO MY FATHER

Whose interest in the past
Became my own

PREFACE

In an age of space exploration it is once more possible to sense the mood of excitement that gripped people in the course of the exploration of Africa during the 19th century. Individuals and institutions made possible the journeys and expeditions that opened the secrets of an unknown continent to the interested public of the Western World. Societies and journals were created to sponsor and record the exploits of public heroes such as David Livingstone, John Speke and Henry Stanley, who followed an earlier generation of unsung, sympathetic observers such as Mungo Park and Heinrich Barth. The penetration of the last frontiers on all continents ultimately deprived us of that unique spirit which accompanied the discovery of new lands. In particular, geographers have tended to depreciate the accomplishments of the better explorers, and have often failed to recognize their dedication to recording and interpreting within the limits of 19th century science and their own skills.

The excitement of discovery is not limited to finding new rivers and mountains but can also be derived from deciphering the history of the physical environment. The pioneer geologist J. W. Gregory certainly experienced as keen a stimulus in first probing into the evolution of the Kenya Rift during his travels of 1893 as any quest into terrae incognitae might have produced. Admittedly many landscapes have by now given up their secrets to an endless succession of natural scientists, but large tracts of our planet still await discovery by anyone who has eyes to see. This is so in many of the great deserts where vistas of incomparable grandeur speak volumes to those who can read the clues. The same is also true of the tropics where cloud-bound mountains and timeless savanna plains often continue to elude rational explanation. Western Ethiopia and northern Kenya are lands such as this, where the sense of undisturbed wilderness can be appreciated on the craggy precipices of uninhabited mountains, along the white sands that rim the Jade Sea, Rudolf, or in endless green forests that seem to swallow the brown river waters cascading from highland bastions. Each landscape is different, each has its own esthetic spell, and each is rich in history, waiting to be deciphered and told.

I owe a particular debt to F. Clark Howell, formerly of Chicago and now of Berkeley, who opened tropical Africa to me in 1967 by bringing me into the International Omo Expedition. During the course of the field seasons in 1967-1969 he made possible my wide-ranging studies in the pursuit of diverse geographical interests, by his encouragement, interest and friendship. The opportunity itself was given through the insight of H. I. M.

Emperor Haile Selassie, who proposed the expedition, and the many officials, Ethiopian and Kenyan, who made it a reality. The Chicago contingent was generously supported by the National Science Foundation under grants GS-1471 and GS-2506. As is the case in any group effort, assistance was freely given and ideas shared. Thus I owe debts of gratitude to each of the colleagues, students and other professionals that at one time or other were part of our expedition. Here I can only single out a few: Frank Brown (Berkeley), who introduced me to the local geology; Claudia Carr (Santa Cruz), who helped me to understand local plant ecology and land use; Atiko Akiru of Lopemkat repeatedly served as a most knowledgeable informant on local matters; and above all, David Woodhead, a fine companion, who piloted the trusted helicopter that carried us in and out of hundreds of landings in a wild land that often defies all other forms of transportation. It was in 1969, standing beside the twisted metal of that same helicopter, crashed at the hands of another pilot, that I realized how much Dave Woodhead had been a part of my work. I hope he will find in these pages a small reflection of the kaleidoscope of scenery, ideas and sheer excitement that we shared on those memorable trips.

In the preparation of this monograph many more people have aided generously and patiently. The climatic and hydrographic data were transcribed for me by Godana Tuni, Chief of the National Climatological Service of Ethiopia; E. F. Lawes, S. E. L. Mukhwana and U. B. Lifiga of the East African Meteorological Department; Alv Svaeren of the Water Development Division, Nairobi; Kamal Ali Mohammed, Chief Engineer Hydrologist of the Sudanese Ministry of Irrigation; Attia Khalil Shaker, Hydrological Inspector of the Nile Control, Cairo; and M. J. Mann, Inland Fisheries Biologist of the FAO at Bujumbura. Hideo Suzuki (University of Tokyo) kindly provided me with a series of unpublished climatological charts; Mary Galneder and Jean Ray, map librarians at the University of Wisconsin and Southern Illinois University respectively, sent me Xeroxes of several maps not locally available. Stefan Hastenrath (University of Wisconsin), Barbara Bell (Harvard), and John Griffiths (Texas A & M University) provided discussion and suggestions on the climatological problems, and both Hastenrath and Michael Sabbagh (University of Texas) read drafts of the climatological sections; J. R. Swart (Kaalam Mission) gave much of his time in the field, in answering my incessant questions and in providing me with an outboard to crisscross the delta waterways; Swart and Carr both read drafts of the chapters on land use; the sedimentological work was carried out with assistance of Carr and of Bruce Gladfelter (Chicago Circle), and Emmett Schulte (University of Wisconsin) kindly arranged a number of special soil analyses; Robert Campbell (Nairobi) provided me with a collection of the aerial photography he shot, with Keith Mousley (Nairobi) at the controls of the Piper Cherokee; and Eva Duncan deserves much credit for typing the manuscript. Hailu Wolde Emmanuel, Imperial Ethiopian Government Ministry of Land Reform and Administration, helped in many ways. Last but not least, I am grateful to John Kirchner for the superb cartography, to the Geography Department of the University of Chicago for subsidizing the cartographic expenses, and to the National Science Foundation (grant GS-27768 to F. C. Howell) for making publication possible in its present format.

Flossmoor and Chicago, Illinois   Karl W. Butzer
June, 1971

This is Contribution No. 25 of the Omo Research Expedition (University of Chicago Group).

TABLE OF CONTENTS

LIST OF TABLES

LIST OF FIGURES

CHAPTER 1

GEOGRAPHICAL SETTING OF THE OMO DELTA

Cieli azzurri, dolci aure native
dove sereno
il mio mattin brillò;
verdi colli, profumate rive,
oh patria mia,
mai più ti rivedrò.

--Aida, Act III

The Rudolf Basin

Lake Rudolf and its catchment form one of the largest non-outlet basins of East Africa. Located at the northern end of the Eastern Rift, the Rudolf Basin consists of an elongated complex of irregular segments extending from near the equator ($0°3'N$) to the summits of Ethiopia ($9°22'N$) (Fig. 1-1). The total area, some 146,000 square kilometers, is relatively small in relation to the size of the lake (about 7500 sq. km.) (Table 1-1). About a half of this catchment contributes little to the lake, at least not with the present climate. The 20- to 30-kilometer radius of lower-order tributaries flowing directly to the lake is situated in an arid environment, where runoff is sporadic and incidental. Of potentially greater importance are the large river systems--Suam, Turkwell and Kerio--draining the Uganda Escarpment to the southwest. Yet, despite impressive discharge rates in the high, well-watered country, these streams only reach the shores of Lake Rudolf in occasional spates; their contribution is now primarily made in the form of seepage. In the past the southern part of the drainage basin was larger, including the arid Suguta Depression and the Baringo Basin (Table 1-1), but such a situation has not applied since mid-Pleistocene times. The principal affluent has always been and remains the Omo River.

The Omo is the largest river of western Ethiopia. Including the Kibish and several other streams that now rarely reach the delta confluence, this part of the basin measures about 84,000 square kilometers--approximately the size of Lake Superior. The river flows 1000 kilometers from the Blue Nile and Sobat watersheds to the shores of Lake Rudolf at $4°29'N$. Much of the main catchment, north of $6°$ latitude, lies at elevations of 2000 to 3000 meters, with the highest peaks (Mt. Gughe, 4203m; Mt. Gurage, 3721m) rivalling those of the world's great mountain belts. The waters of the upper Omo and the

1

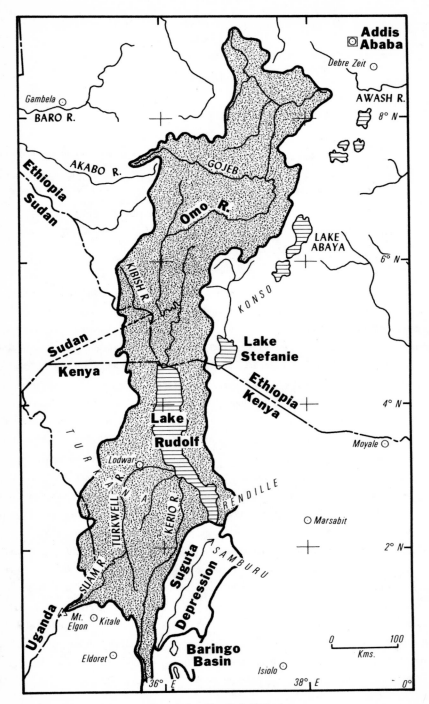

Fig. 1-1. The Rudolf Basin

TABLE 1-1

APPROXIMATE DIMENSIONS OF THE LAKE RUDOLF BASIN
(in square kilometers)

Catchment	Total Area	Above 1000m
Omo River	73,000	60,000
Sanderson's "Gulf"	11,000	2,500
Rudolf Littoral	15,000	1,000
Lake Rudolf	7,500	---
Turkwell-Suam River	24,500	15,500
Lomenyangaparat	3,500	500
Kerio River	13,500	9,500
Total	146,000	89,000
Suguta Depression	13,000	7,500
Baringo Basin	5,500	5,500

Greater, Lesser, and Jimma Ghibé tumble over a series of cataracts through the 160-kilometer canyon of the Omo, through gorges up to 600 meters deep (Merla, 1963) (see Fig. 1-2). After merging with the waters of the Gojeb the canyon gradually opens up into an entrenched valley (Fig. 1-3), ultimately to emerge onto a broad tectonic depression at the northern end of the Rudolf trough. The level of Rudolf is at about 375 meters,[1] giving the Omo drainage basin considerable potential energy, with a mean river gradient of 27:10,000.

The delta plain of the Omo is situated in the far southwestern corner of Ethiopia, near the intersection of the borders of Ethiopia, Kenya, and the Sudan (Fig. 1-2). It has a total area of about 1600 square kilometers, but depending on the fluctuations in the level of Lake Rudolf, the delta plain has been rapidly and repeatedly submerged or laid dry during the last several centuries. Lying west of, and partly interlocking with the delta, is a second depression known as Sanderson's Gulf.[2] This is a poorly-defined, elongated zone of

[1] Maps since the 1930's generally give the level of Lake Rudolf as 369m (1230 ft), regardless of the fact that the level has fluctuated repeatedly within a range of about 5m. Since 1967 the level is probably close to 375m, although all elevations from this part of East Africa are approximations--often obtained by averaging conflicting triangulation values. Recently, a corrected elevation of 345m has been cited (Gwynne, 1970), although without specifying which techniques were employed to obtain it. Since a revision of 30m would require readjustment of many elevations in the study area, the 375m value will continue to be used here.

[2] Named in 1898 by Austin (1899), at a time when the lake was high. The designation

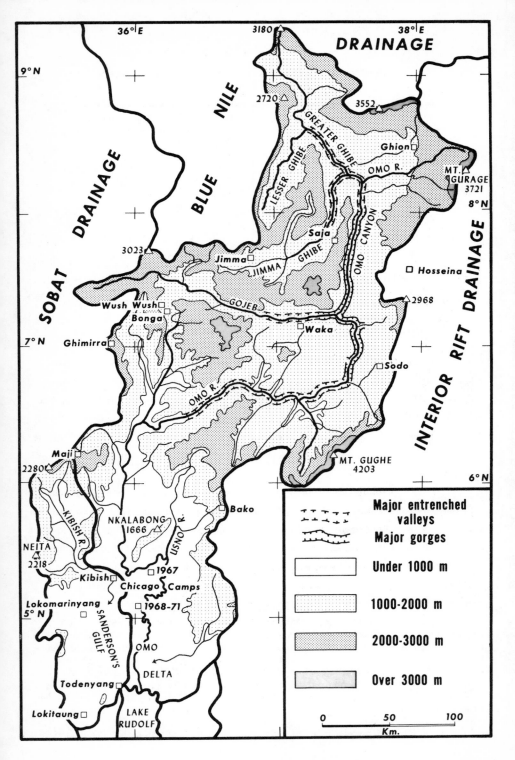

Fig. 1-2. Topography of the Omo Basin

about 750 square kilometers that has sometimes functioned as an extension of Lake Rudolf and now serves as an overflow basin for water from the Omo River.

The Problem

The major deltas of the world are found along the continental margins. Many of them have been studied intensively by geologists and geomorphologists, primarily with economic motives such as petroleum resources and land use. Yet next to no geomorphologic study has been undertaken of lake deltas and none whatsoever of deltas terminating in non-outlet lakes. The levels of lakes are unstable, particularly in endorheic basins of arid regions, and deltas in such settings will be subject to repeated and rapid changes of base level. Consequently it is to be expected that deltas in non-outlet lakes undergo almost continuous readjustments. By the standards of marine or estuarine deltas, that of the Omo River is small. But it does provide a classic example of a delta prograded into a non-outlet lake, Rudolf.

The evolution of a delta such as that of the Mississippi (see Bernard and LeBlanc, 1965), can be traced through a series of deep profiles that record vertical and lateral sequences of sediments over tens or hundreds of millennia. For shorter time intervals such an approach is less suitable than the areal study of surficial forms and deposits. This is the case in the Omo Delta, where the history of the past millennium is vividly recorded in changing meander belts, successive distributary clusters, and several sets of beach ridges.

Lake Rudolf, the last of the great African lakes to be discovered by European explorers, is also the least understood. The topography of the drainage basin, the basic hydrologic system, and even the lake level are known in a rudimentary way only. Yet it is precisely an enigmatic setting such as this that provides a challenge to search for basic facts and seek more comprehensive understanding. The Omo Delta is but a finite unit of the Rudolf Basin, but it is here that a great river merges with a great lake, at this moment in time, in interaction with the elements of the entire basin. The task of fully understanding the Omo Delta is, therefore, a formidable one and one for which the data are still inadequate. Within these and other practical limitations, imposed by time and resources, it has been attempted to discern and explain the physical landscape of that delta. The picture so derived reflects the bias of a geomorphologist, but the implications for an understanding of climatic variability and ecology in a broader African perspective seem considerable.

"Gulf" is of course inappropriate today. Strictly speaking, the 1896 term of Inganno's Gulf (Vannutelli and Citerni, 1897, 1899) has precedence.

6

Fig. 1-3. The incised, middle Omo Valley. July 1968 (K. W. B.)

Fig. 1-4. The Turkwell and Kerio Deltas (left to right). August 1967 (K. W. B.)

Early Observations in the Rudolf Basin

The Rudolf Basin first entered the historical pale during the late 16th century, when Ethiopia conquered parts of the upper Omo Basin (1586-95). As a consequence António Fernandes and Fequr Egzi'e, emissaries of the emperor Susenyos, travelled through part of that area in 1613-14, preparing a record that is fortunately preserved in the 1646 description of Manoel de Almeida, a Portuguese Jesuit (see Beckingham and Huntingford, 1954: 29, 155, 157).[3] Only in 1843 did the brothers Antoine and Arnaud d'Abbadie first explore the uppermost Omo, providing a wealth of observations complemented in 1880 by Antonio Cecchi and 1882 by Paul Soleillet. At the southern end of the Rudolf catchment, Mount Elgon and Lake Baringo were explored by Joseph Thomson in 1883, although both Baringo and Rudolf were known directly to the Zanzibari traders by or shortly after 1880 (Oliver and Mathew, 1963: 316f.). The subsequent discovery of Rudolf and of the Omo Delta by Samuel Teleki and Ludwig Höhnel in 1888 hardly comes as a surprise. What is important is that Höhnel[4] was a good observer of ethnological and geological features, his data allowing Eduard Suess to first postulate the existence of the Great Rift (Höhnel et al., 1891).[5]

It is curious that the course of the Omo River remained uncertain until 1896, when Vittorio Bòttego led an expedition down the valley of the middle Omo,[6] showing conclusively

---

[3]It includes a graphic commentary on the upper Omo Canyon, and speculation that the Omo River empties into the Indian Ocean near Malindi, i.e. identifying it with the Tana. Fernandes must be credited as the first European to see the Omo River.

[4]Ludwig Ritter von Höhnel was born in Pressburg (Bratislava) in 1857, entered the Austrian naval academy at Fiume (Rijeka) 1873 and was promoted to battleship ensign 1879. At the suggestion of Crown Prince Rudolf he was chosen to accompany Count Samuel Teleki von Szék (1845-1916) on a hunting safari to East Africa. The young lieutenant then succeeded in persuading Teleki to explore the unknown Ethiopian borderlands. The expedition left the coast of Tanzania in February, 1887, reached Lake Rudolf via Baringo March 5, 1888, the Omo Delta April 4, discovering Lake Stefanie April 18, and returning to the coast in October, 1888 (Höhnel, 1894; also Richards, 1961: 100-113). A second expedition in eastern Kenya (1892-93) terminated when Höhnel was incapacitated by a charging rhino. His last visit to East Africa, in 1905, saw him conclude a commercial treaty with the Emperor of Ethiopia. Höhnel retired as a rear-admiral in 1909, but remained intellectually active until his death in Vienna at the age of 85 (see Höhnel, 1938).

[5]Höhnel (1890, 1894) provided a 1:750,000 sketch map of Lake Rudolf and the mouth of the Omo Delta, estimating the lake surface as 9000 sq. km. (probably nearer 7900 sq. km. at that time), and calculating lake level at 400m (although closer to 383m) on the basis of boiling-point temperatures. His records can be utilized to reconstruct the delta morphology and lake level (see chapter 3), as well as assess delta land-use (see chapter 4) in 1888.

[6]This ill-fated Italian expedition moved through southern Ethiopia unaware that an Italian army had been decisively defeated at Adua (March 1, 1896). Surprised by 2 Ethiopian columns on the middle Omo (July 1, 1896), Bòttego eluded them by a series of forced

that this mighty river debouched into Lake Rudolf (Vannutelli and Citerni, 1899).[7] Bòttego was accompanied by a geographer, Maurizio Sacchi,[8] who recognized extensive lacustrine deposits in the lower Omo Basin (D'Ossat and Millosevich, 1900) and made a variety of meteorological notations (Vannutelli and Citerni, 1899: Appendix 4). During the following years a succession of visitors passed rapidly through the Delta, including E. Brumpt (see Bourg de Bozas, 1903), who in 1902 discovered rich fossiliferous exposures, the so-called Omo Beds that were to attract scientists decades later. Extensive topographic mapping accompanied the first border delimitation between Ethiopia and Kenya in 1903 (Maud, 1904) with another attempt at demarcation in 1908 (Gwynn, 1911).

This first phase of exploration was not followed up for over 2 decades, due to the unrest of the border tribes, the British pacification of Turkana (1914-26), and the closing of the Ethiopian frontier. A new phase of reconnaissance was inagurated 1930-31 by the Cambridge Expedition to Lake Rudolf (see Fuchs, 1934; Worthington, 1932), continued in 1934 by the extensive geological studies of V. E. Fuchs (1935, 1939) northwest, south and east of the lake. Almost simultaneously, in 1932-33, Camille Arambourg (1935, 1944, 1948) mapped northwest of the lake and studied the fossiliferous Omo Beds west of the Omo Delta. As a consequence of Arambourg's and Fuchs' work, the basic geological framework of the Rudolf region was established. The areas north and east of the delta remained almost unexplored, however, despite some reconnaissance by M. Marchetti and by the Zavattari Expedition of 1939, the results of which were incorporated into Dainelli's (1943) fundamental study on the geology of Ethiopia. Partial aerial photography was flown by the RAF 1940-41, but the British campaign did not lead to any systematic work in southwestern Ethiopia.

---

marches, and was able to explore the Lower Omo Basin and the Stefanie area from early August to mid-December, 1896, although many members of the party were down with malaria most of this time. The hostility of the Turkana later prevented Bòttego from returning southward along the western shores of Rudolf. Instead he turned north, skirting the western foothills of Ethiopia where he was killed in a brief encounter, north of Gambela, March 14, 1897. After several months of imprisonment the survivors of the party were allowed to proceed via Addis Abeba to Djibouti (Vannutelli and Citerni, 1897, 1899).

[7] The 1:1 million aeronautical chart (U.S. Air Force, 1966: sheet ONC L-5) inexplicably labels the lower Omo as the Ghibé River, while older, Italian maps use "Omo Bòttego." The river is locally known as Warr in the delta, as Nanam, Anam or Nianam by tribes a little further upstream.

[8] Dr. Sacchi was to return directly from the Omo Delta to Somalia. While a caravan with most of his mineralogical and molluscan collections (some 350 samples) and all his notes eventually reached the coast safely, Sacchi returned to Lake Abaya to collect a cache of rock samples left there earlier in the year. Here he was murdered by a group of Amharic marauders (Feb. 7, 1897). His collections and notes were analyzed and published posthumously at the University of Rome (D'Ossat and Millosevich, 1900).

Recent Studies

A new period of intensive and rapidly accelerating research in the Rudolf area began in 1959, with study by Whitworth (1965) of late Quaternary deposits northwest of the lake, and the multidisciplinary work of the Harvard Expedition to the west and southwest (Patterson, 1966; Patterson et al., 1970). Since 1968 R. E. F. Leakey has organized a highly successful survey of early, fossil-bearing deposits northeast of the lake, a part of the basin previously quite unknown (Leakey and others, 1970). Also, in 1968, a South Turkana Expedition has been engaged in topographic and geologic work southwest of Rudolf (Gwynne, 1970; Rhemtulla, 1970).

In 1959 F. C. Howell (then of the University of Chicago) obtained permission to enter Ethiopia to re-examine the fossiliferous Omo Beds, a consequence of which was the international Omo Research Expedition of 1967-1971, jointly organized by L. S. B. Leakey, Arambourg and Howell, and enjoying the full support of the Imperial Ethiopian Government. A group from the National Museum of Kenya (R. E. F. and Margaret Leakey) during part of 1967 searched for fossils in the north-central part of the Lower Omo Basin. The French team (Arambourg, Y. Coppens, J. Chavaillon, R. Bonnefille) concentrated on the fossils of the Omo Beds, working each summer since 1967 (Arambourg et al., 1969; Bonnefille et al., 1970). The group based on the University of Chicago, supported by the National Science Foundation, has included members from that university (Howell, K. W. Butzer, G. Eck and C. J. Carr), the University of California (F. H. Brown), and the Rijksuniversiteit Gent (J. de Heinzelin). With the aid of the Wenner-Gren Foundation, Brown was able to initiate the geological work of the Chicago Expedition in 1966. During the subsequent summers (1967-68) this multidisciplinary effort undertook a more systematic general study of the Lower Omo Basin, prior to focusing on the fossiliferous Omo Beds during the 1969-70 seasons, with further collecting and excavation projected for 1971. This more comprehensive work of the Chicago Expedition was made possible by 3 to 5 Land Rovers, a 4-wheel drive truck and, for part of the time, by charter of a Hughes-300 helicopter and a Piper Cherokee aircraft, all kept in communication by radio, to avoid fatal breakdowns or accidents in difficult or almost intraversible terrain. The helicopter, in fact, was a total loss after crashing in July, 1969.

The study of the contemporary Omo Delta reported on here was carried out as part of the Chicago effort. After brief helicopter survey in 1967, the available air photos[9]

---

[9] The Royal Air Force flew aerial photography of the lower Omo Valley on 3 occasions between 1957 and 1959, printed at scales varying from 1:77,000 to 1:92,000. Vertical and horizontal ground control was limited, however, so that no contour lines could be provided for either the 1:250,000 reconnaissance map published by the East African Survey in 1943 (Sheet 1497, "Lokitaung-Omo River," reprinted by Federal Survey Squadron, Royal Engineers, 1958) or the 1:100,000 series prepared by the Survey of Kenya in 1961 (Series

were studied and the wealth of incidental travellers' reports evaluated. The major field
mapping was undertaken in 1968 on the basis of helicopter runs and groundwork, a motor-
boat traverse of all open waterways, and the aerial photography. C. J. Carr, otherwise
engaged in study of the plant ecology of the Omo floodplain and the adjacent upland plains,
participated in this phase of the work and made a reconnaissance of the delta vegetation
(Carr, n.d.). In 1969 the interim 1:100,000 geomorphological map was checked out in the
field, with further mapping on the northeastern margins of the delta (see the preliminary
report, Butzer, 1970). Finally, the entire maps were revised in 1970 using the excellent
air photos kindly made available late in 1969 by the Ethiopian Mapping and Geography Institute. Carr collected additional soil samples in 1969 and 1970, and independently investi-
gated land use along the western delta margins.

A Geological Framework for the Lower Omo Basin

Geological Antecedents. The Omo Delta is situated in a complex tectonic depression, known as the Lower Omo Basin[10] (Figs. 1-1 and 1-5) and forming an extension of the
Lake Rudolf trough. Structural controls are particularly apparent in the large-scale topographic lineaments of this sector of East Africa, even though detailed studies are lacking.[11]
So, for example, the Omo drainage shows a striking geometric arrangement of its principal streams, suggesting successive accretions of the headwater segments of rivers once
draining to the Sobat and Blue Nile Rivers. Similarly, the lower Omo and the Usno River
are aligned with the quasi-rectilinear shorelines that bound the northern half of Lake
Rudolf. Such superficial observations can, however, do scant justice to the complexity of
the large-scale fault and fold patterns.

Y633 Edition 1 GSGS, War Office and Air Ministry, London; sheet 4a, "Namuruputh, " covers the western periphery of the Delta while sheet 5, "Ileret, " shows the southeastern
extremity). Since the Omo Delta lies within Ethiopian territory the relevant sheets of the
latter series remain unpublished, and the best available map is the 1:250,000 series of the
Survey of Kenya with a contour interval of 150 meters (Series Y503, Survey of Kenya, 1961;
sheets NB-36-16, "Lokitaung, " and NB-37-13, "Stefanie"). In 1965-67, as part of a U.S.A.-
Ethiopian mapping mission, the U. S. Air Force flew excellent air photo coverage of the
entire delta area, printed at scales typically ranging from 1:52,000 to 1:63,000. These
photos will ultimately be employed to draft accurate maps of the study area; unfortunately
these American photos were not available to either the Ethiopian government or the expedition before 1969. Of further use are two Gemini IV satellite photos (NASA nos. S-65-
34796/7).

[10]This designation is used and broadly defined by Merla (1963, see especially his
plate 2).

[11]Structural features of northwestern Kenya are mapped by Walsh and Dodson (1969).
For the Ethiopian sector, previous published information was limited to the somewhat controversial structural overview by Merla (1963) at 1:3,520,000.

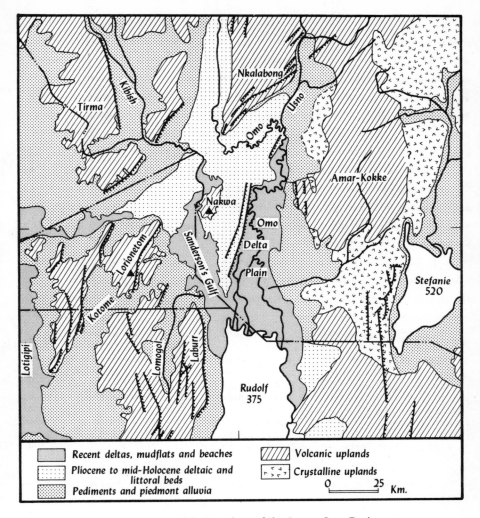

Fig. 1-5. Simplified Geology of the Lower Omo Basin

The regional basement is formed by Precambrian metamorphics, primarily gneisses and amphibolites with intrusions of granite and pegmatite (Arambourg, 1944; Brown, n.d.). These crystalline rocks appear to have been bevelled by one or more peri- ods of planation during late Cretaceous to early Tertiary times (see Saggerson and Baker, 1965), in part prior to accumulation of the first known sedimentaries, the Turkana Grits, a suite of up to 300 meters of coarse arcosic sandstones, grits, and quartz conglomerates (Walsh and Dodson, 1969; Arambourg, 1944; Arambourg and Wolff, 1969). The sand grains include subrounded quartz, altered feldspars, micas, and ferromagnesians derived from the Precambrian "Basement Complex" and probably deposited in a terrestrial or lacustrine environment. The Turkana Grits (or comparable detrital beds) are locally inter- calated with and then overlain by a massive series of extrusive vulcanics, totalling over

1500 meters in thickness. Basalts and rhyolites are dominant, with limited development of phonolites, nephelinites, and andesites. Potassium-argon dates suggest that these extrusives range in age from late Oligocene to late Miocene or early Pliocene.[12]

Downwarping of the floor of the Eastern Rift Valley seems to have begun by early Miocene times, but major faulting and folding in the Lake Rudolf area appears to date from the Pliocene.[13] Be this as it may, the Lower Omo Basin must have been created along essentially modern lines during the first part of the Pliocene period, since a series of deltaic, fluvial and lacustrine sediments were already accumulating by 4.4 million years ago.[14] These are part of the Omo Group (which includes the Omo Beds) and consist of clays, silts, arcosic sands, and reworked tuffs with a stratigraphic thickness totalling over 850 meters and some 19 potassium-argon dates ranging from 4.40 to 1.81 million years (Butzer, 1971a; De Heinzelin et al., 1971; Brown and Lajoie, 1971) (see Table 1-2 for stratigraphic outline). The molluscan and fish faunas as well as the topography indicate that a series of interconnected depressions intermittently linked the ancestral lakes of the Omo-Rudolf trough with the Nile system.[15] The Omo Beds west of the Delta were intensively fractured

---

[12]See Walsh and Dodson (1969), and Arambourg (1944: 171ff.). Some 8 potassium argon dates from Turkana have been published by Reilly et al. (1966). They are as follows: (a) Augite and analcime basalts: 20.7, 23.0, 31.5, and 32.3 million years, with reversed polarity; (b) Olivine basalts: 23.3 and 23.5 million years, with reversed polarity; (c) Phonolites and nephelinites, 12.5 and 14.9 million years, with normal polarity; and (d) rhyolites and andesites, undated. These ages compare with those obtained from western Uganda and more southerly portions of the Eastern Rift, namely 23 to 17.5 million years for the older group of nephelinite lavas and pyroclastics, 14 to 11.5 million years for the younger "plateau" phonolites (Bishop et al., 1969). The flood basalts that mantle the middle and upper Omo Basin (see Mohr, 1964, with 1:2 million folding map) are probably of Oligocene age (see Mohr, 1968), while the superimposed shield volcanoes, such as Mts. Gughe and Gurage, were built up during the early Miocene; following an extended period of uplift and planation, welded tuffs were extensively laid down on the upland surfaces in late Pliocene times.

[13]See Saggerson and Baker (1965); Walsh and Dodson (1969); also McCall et al. (1967) and Baker and Wohlenberg (1971). The orogenic periods leading to major uplift of the Ethiopian Plateau appear to have been broadly synchronous with those of Kenya. Mohr (1968) places the major rift-faulting and updoming in the early to middle Miocene, with at least 2 phases of renewed uplift during Plio-Pleistocene times.

[14]Comparable lacustrine and fluvial sediments, but with more appreciable pyroclastic components (Lothagam "2" and "3"), were accumulating in one or more basins southwest of Lake Rudolf only slightly earlier (see Patterson et al., 1970).

[15]Of 9 mulluscan species identified from the Omo Group so far, 7 are today found in the Nile system, while the remaining 2 are present in Lake Rudolf as well as in other East African lakes (see Roger, 1944). Of 9 fish genera recognized, 8 are found in the Nile system of which 7 still count among the modern fish genera of Lake Rudolf (Arambourg, 1948: 469ff., 496; also Worthington and Ricardo, 1935). In fact, it is probable that the Plio-Pleistocene Umm Ruwaba Series of the Sudan (see Butzer and Hansen, 1968: 255f.; Berry and Whiteman, 1968) is broadly contemporary with the Omo Group and that close connections existed across the southeastern Sudan between the Omo and Paleo-Sudd Basins.

TABLE 1-2

LATE CENOZOIC STRATIGRAPHY OF THE LOWER OMO BASIN

Probable Geological Age	Isotopic Dates	Rock Units			Depositional Environments
		Contemporary deltaic, alluvial and littoral beds			
Holocene	C^{14} 3100-6200 yr C^{14} 7500-9500 yr	KIBISH FM. (115m)		Mb. IVb	Deltaic, littoral
				Mb. IVa	Deltaic, littoral
Upper Pleistocene	K/Ar "O" C^{14} 37,000 yr			(Nakwa tuffs and basalt extrusions)	
				Mb. III	Deltaic, littoral
				Mb. II	Deltaic
Middle Pleistocene	Th/U 130,000 yr			Mb. I	Deltaic
		(One or more episodes of faulting of Shungura Fm.) (Renewed sedimentation west of modern delta)			
Lower Pleistocene		(Faulting of Shungura Fm.)			
	K/Ar 1.81-3.75 mill. yr	OMO GROUP	SHUNGURA FM. ("Omo Beds") (600m)		Alluvial, deltaic, littoral, lacustrine
	K/Ar 3.95 mill. yr		NKALABONG FM. (88m)		Alluvial, littoral-lacustrine, eolian
to			(Faulting, local or general)		
	K/Ar 4.05-4.4 mill. yr		MURSI FM. (148m)	Mb. IV	Basalt
				Mbs. I-III	Deltaic, littoral alluvial
Upper Pliocene		(Downwarping and downfaulting of Omo Basin and Rudolf Rift, one or more major episodes)			
Lower Pliocene to Lower Miocene		(Repeated volcanic episodes with massive basalt and rhyolite extrusions over pre-existing erosional surfaces developed on the Basement Complex; followed by cutting of one or more planation surfaces)			

in mid-Pleistocene times, when the present structural patterns were accentuated or finally established.

Structural Patterns. In a general way, the modern Omo Delta is bounded by several sets of en échelon faults to the east, and by a system of fractured, plunging folds to the west.

East of the delta plain lies the Amar-Kokke Highland, with elevations of 1000 to 2000 meters, forming a horst-like structure between the Omo River and Lake Stefanie (Schottenloher, 1938; Nowack, 1954: 16ff.). Most of this upland is formed of metamorphic rocks, partly capped by Tertiary or more recent extrusives (Fig. 1-5). Horst structures are clearly visible from the air to the west of Lake Stefanie. The fractures adjacent to the Omo valley are more difficult to pinpoint among alluvium-veneered pediment surfaces cut into the Basement Complex, and a major set of en échelon faults appears to strike almost due north, delimiting the late Cenozoic fill and Basement Complex to the east of the Omo Delta and the Omo and Usno floodplains (Fig. 1-5).

West of the delta plain there is a series of faulted, plunging anticlinal ridges that expose Basement Complex, such as at the base of Mt. Laburr; sediments of the Omo Group, such as between Kaalam and Shungura; or, elsewhere, massive Tertiary basalts and rhyolites (see Walsh and Dodson, 1969). These plunging anticlines are badly fractured, primarily by steep tensional faults that cut longitudinally through the folds. Downfaulting is to the east, i.e. toward the Omo Delta and Lake Rudolf, while warped sediments or asymmetrical folds dip in a westerly direction. Northwest and north of the delta, the strata of the Omo Group are fractured by 3 or more major faults striking N 0 to $25°$ E. Vertical throws may be as much as 100 meters and cumulative displacement is substantially greater (De Heinzelin et al., 1971). The Nakwa volcanics were probably extruded along a related tensional fissure during the late Pleistocene (see Brown and Carmichael, 1969).

The synclinal depressions further to the west of the delta include the Lotogipi Plain, the Kotome and Lomogol valleys, and Sanderson's Gulf. These are fringed by alluvial fans and filled with fine-grained alluvium, in large part of post-Pleistocene age. Pediments are widely developed, under alluvium, along the margins of these depressions. The Nkalabong Range, further to the north, is largely composed of Miocene rhyolites, truncated by one or more major faults to the southeast, with strata dipping to the northwest at 20 to 30 degrees. Superimposed late Pliocene extrusives dip at only about half this angle (Brown, n.d.). The structure of the remaining highlands on the northwestern and northeastern peripheries of the Lower Omo Basin is next to unknown.

In retrospect, the Omo delta plain is situated in a faulted syncline between two structural provinces: the Amar-Kokke horst to the east, the basin-and-range structures of the faulted, plunging folds to the west.

Recent Geological History. The vicissitudes of Lake Rudolf since the last major tectonic "accidents" are now well understood as a result of studies in the Lower Omo Basin, where a mid-Pleistocene to mid-Holocene time span is represented by the littoral, deltaic and fluvial beds of the Kibish Formation (Butzer et al., 1970) (see Table 1-2). The oldest of these units lie just beyond the satisfactory radiocarbon dating range (Member III, greater than 37,000 B. P.) to as much as 130,000 years or more (a thorium–uranium date on Member I); each of these earlier sediment sequences indicates a lake level of +60 to +70 meters, with the Omo Delta located 70 to 100 kilometers north of its present position, and hydrographic connections indicated to the Lotogipi Plain and probably the Nile system.[16] No sedimentary record is known from the period 35,000 to 9500 B. P., but the lake must have been relatively low during most of this time and there are some indications of local aridity such as carbonate horizons and "desert" varnish on lag pebbles.

Several centuries before 9500 B. P. the lake must have risen rapidly, and the lake level subsequently fluctuated between about +60 and +80 until about 7500 B. P. (Member IVa, Kibish Fm.), when Lake Rudolf shrank to about its present dimensions (Butzer, Isaac et al., 1971; Robbins, n.d.). The youngest transgressive sequence (Member IVb, Kibish Fm.) preserves considerable surface morphology; the lake level was at +15 meters ca. 6600 B. P. rising to a maximum of +65 to +70 meters by ca. 6200 B. P., sustained until after 4400 B. P. Following a temporary regression of unknown amplitude, a final transgression to +70 meters is indicated a little before 3000 B. P.[17] Lake Rudolf has been relatively low since that time, dropping rapidly, in successive stages, below the threshold of the probable Nile overflow. Concomitantly, the lower Omo River cut down its bed by as much as 52 meters before it could begin to aggrade its modern floodplain and delta.

Consequently, the modern delta plain is a remarkably recent phenomenon: the basal deposits are younger than 3 millennia. Equally surprising is the fact that a major delta has been situated somewhere in the Lower Omo Basin for most of the last 5 million years. The facies of the Omo Beds and of the Kibish Formation are quite similar and, except for reworked tuffs, appear to have close analogs in the modern delta sediments. With such a continuity of depositional environments, investigation of the modern delta assumes added significance for interpretation of the older beds.

---

[16] Roger (1944: 147) identified 18 molluscan species in the equivalent of the Kibish Formation, of which 10 are common to the Nile system, 7 others are found in one or other of the East African lakes, while the remaining species is endemic to Lake Rudolf. Of 21 molluscan species present in Lake Rudolf today, 16 are nilotic and only 2 are endemic. The situation is similar for the fish fauna: 26 of 38 species and subspecies in the modern lake are common to the Nile system of the Sudan (Worthington and Ricardo, 1935). Only 7 species and 4 subspecies are endemic and these as well as the endemic mollusc are clearly derived from nilotic forms. This evidence would suggest that although connections with the Pibor–Sobat drainage were real, they were nonetheless tenuous. During moist years there may have been a temporary or seasonal overflow of water into the poorly-defined drainage channels of the southeastern Sudan.

[17] 3250 ± 150 B. P. (L-1203-H). Calibrated to true calendar years by the Stuiver-Suess correction formula this gives 1500 ± 150 B. C., while the fluctuations of the bristle-cone pine radiocarbon curve indicate that a date of 1650 ± 150 B. C. provides an even closer approximation.

Information on Vegetation and Soils of the Omo Basin

The present status of studies on the vegetation and soils of the Omo Basin is unsat-
isfactory. Nonetheless, the available information is relevant to understanding the hydrology of the basin and the nature of the sediment yield.

The Vegetation Cover. Useful overviews of the natural and actual vegetation of the
highlands have been provided by Picchi-Sermolli (1957) and Logan (1946), with complemen-
tary information from Zavattari (1941), Scott (1952), Kuls (1958: 23ff.), and Hedberg (1962).
The plant ecology of the plains and riverine environments of the lower basin has been
studied by Carr (n.d.). These sources can be utilized to attempt an outline of the vegetation cover of the Omo catchment (see Fig. 1-6A).

The plains that floor the Lower Omo Basin are in part well-drained, in part seasonally wet. The well-drained, lowland surfaces at 400-500 meters (e.g. beach ridges and
higher interridge terrain) have a tree-shrub savanna[18] including such elements as Maerua
crassifolia, Grewia tenax, Cordia gharaf and Sporobolus marginatus, with many succu-
lents and much bare ground present in rapidly drained "badlands" or on excessively permeable substrata (Carr, n.d.). The contiguous piedmont and foothill country (at 450-600m),
generally more sandy, has a thorny scrub or thicket, with patches of shrub steppe. The
seasonally-wet, lower-lying plains (at 400-450m) are characterized by grassland savanna
or, on less waterlogged soils, a shrub savanna with Acacia horrida and A. paoli (Carr,
n.d.).[19] In contrast, the levees of the Omo River and, to a lesser extent, of the other
floodplains, have a closed galeria woodland, or forest, of which the most mesic associa-
tions include Trichilia roka, Tapura fischeri, Ficus sycomorus, Celtis integrifolia,
Ziziphus pubescens and Cordia gharaf. The delta flats and flood basins are significantly
more disturbed and mantled with tree-shrub savanna, shrub steppe or shrub thickets that,
in the delta fringe, go over into a complex of wetland vegetation (Cyperus, Phragmites,
Typha) and open water (Carr, n.d.).

At elevations of 800 to 1200 meters, this thorn savanna is replaced by a more mesic
vegetation on the low mountains and hilly uplands that fringe the basin. On the wetter parts
of the Amar-Kokke horst (above 1200m) a sclerophyl bush is dominated by Olea chrysophylla,
with abundant lianas and tall, candelabra Euphorbias (Zavattari, 1941). The Nkalabong
Range, on the other hand, is grassy savanna with dispersed fire-tolerant broadleaved trees

---

[18] Broadly equivalent to the "Low Savanna" mapped from airphotos by Lebon (1965:
sheet Uganda-Mongallo) for the adjacent parts of southeastern Sudan. Correspondence
with the successive belts of "Subdesert shrub and grassland," "Xerophilous open woodland"
and "Undifferentiated savanna" mapped and classified by Picchi-Sermolli (1953, 1957) is
more difficult to establish.

[19] Lebon's (1965) "Seasonally-wet grassland of Southern Clay Plain."

17

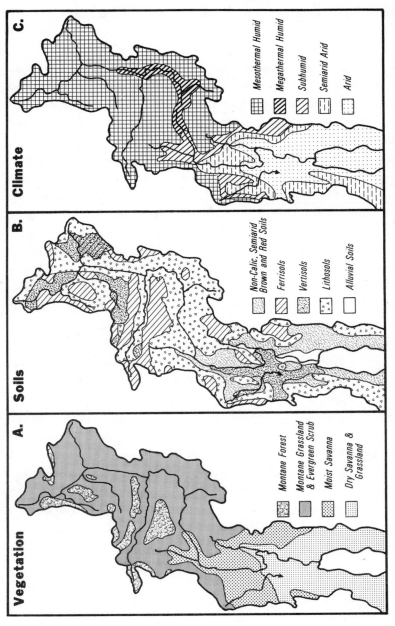

Fig. 1-6A. --Modern Vegetation of the Omo Basin (modified after Logan, 1946, and Picchi-Sermolli, 1957). Fig. 1-6B.--Soil Mantle of the Omo Basin (based, in part, on D'Hoore, 1964). Fig. 1-6C.--Thornthwaite Climates of the Omo Basin (calculated from station data provided by the National Climatological Service of Ethiopia and the East African Meteorological Department). Each of these maps is generalized and approximate.

(Carr, n.d.), giving way to closed woodlands in steep-sided, fire-protected valleys. Comparable, transitional forms of vegetation are fragmentarily preserved on the Lorionetom Range (at 1200-1700m) and the steep eastern slopes of the Tirma Massif. In general, however, the highlands west and northwest of the basin are badly denuded, with sparse, stoney grasslands and extensive rocky slopes.

As yet unstudied are the scrub woodlands that range beyond the northern flanks of Nkalabong and then extend broadly across the flanks of the middle Omo Valley, north of latitude 5°45'. Presumably these grade into the little-known, broadleaved evergreen forests found along the steep slopes of the lower Omo Canyon and several of the narrow tributary valleys (see Kuls, 1958: 26).

The montane rainforest of Ethiopia has been ravaged by man and the surviving remnants show a considerable differentiation. The high plateau east of the Omo has been almost entirely deforested, and those tree stands that remain show little internal variation. Small patches of bamboo scrub, favored by disturbance and man, alternate with evergreen coniferous woodland--dominantly or exclusively Podocarpus, with Juniperus locally prominent (Picchi-Sermolli, 1957: 74f.). Forests are much more extensive on the western plateau, between 1900 and 2500 meters, around Bonga, Ghimirra, Jimma, and among the headwaters of the Gojeb and Ghibé Rivers (see Fig. 1-6A). Presumably indicative of a less accentuated dry season and warmer temperatures than found in other parts of upland Ethiopia, these woodlands are richer in genera, with broadleaved forms dominant: Pouteria, Albizzia, Pygeum, Ekebergia, and Syzygium (Logan, 1946: 28ff.; Picchi-Sermolli, 1957: 82ff.). Trees are structured into several vertical tiers, with tree-ferns, numerous lianas, creepers and epiphytic mosses. By and large however the subtropical to temperate uplands of the Omo Basin have been reduced to cropland, wooded grassland, and degraded evergreen scrub, precariously stocked with herd animals. The resulting cover is much less effective than closed rainforest in retarding runoff and inhibiting soil erosion.

The upper zone of montane rainforest is technically represented by an evergreen coniferous forest, dominated by Hagenia and Schefflera, from about 2400 or 2500 to 3000 meters or more (see Picchi-Sermolli, 1957: 77ff.; Kuls, 1958: 27). Little appears to remain of this vertical unit, even in western Ethiopia, and desolate montane grasslands give way to ericaceous heaths, with Erica arborea, Hypericum and giant lobelias (Scott, 1952; Picchi-Sermolli, 1957: 86ff.).

Soil Types and Soil Erosion. Little is known about the soils of western and southern Ethiopia, although the 1:5 million soils map of Africa (D'Hoore, 1964) shows basic distributions rather crudely and often quite inaccurately, reflecting few direct observations. In collaboration with C. J. Carr, the writer was able to sample soils of the Omo Delta and floodplain and of the adjacent lowlands, with more incidental sampling of the peripheral highlands. These materials were subsequently studied in the laboratory. The soils of the delta and floodplain are described in the subsequent chapter, but a more detailed discussion in a general context must await an extended paper on the geomorphology of the Lower Omo Basin. However, a brief overview is appropriate at this point (see Fig. 1-6B):

(a) The contemporary soils of the delta and floodplain are in the "alluvial" category, with weak horizonation, shallow humification and limited gley characteristics.[20] Organic matter seldom exceeds 1 or 2% and most soil properties, including deep cracking traits, reflect almost exclusively on original sediment properties. As a result, flood silts generally have brown (10 YR hues by the Munsell notation),[21] poorly differentiated A- and B-horizons of silty clay loam, with blocky structure, and occasional, fine limonitic mottling in the subsoil. Basin deposits and clay plugs, on the other hand, have deep, cracking clays of brown to very dark gray color (10 YR hues), strong prismatic structure, silty clay or clay texture, and moderate to intensive mottling. This second category qualifies as a Vertisol (see Dudal, 1965).

(b) The "upland" plains that floor the Lower Omo Basin commonly have impeded drainage after rains, and deep cracking patterns (50-120cm deep) may develop during the drier parts of year when the water-table is low. Dark cracking clay soils of "intrazonal" type are characteristic here, although such vertisols show considerable lateral variation in response to facies changes or surface drainage.[22] In particular, there may be sub-surface accumulations of sodium salts. The well-drained sediments of the Kibish Formation, particularly along the dissected or gullied floodplain margins, show clear AC-profiles, with brown (7.5 to 10 YR hues) A-horizons (50 to 80cm thick) marked by clay mineral formation (montmorillonite), alkaline reactions (pH 6.5-7.4) and a lack of free carbonates. Similar but loamy AC-soils develop on the sandy piedmont alluvia, although deeper, reddish paleosols are found on many older fans, while regosols are commonly produced where fans remain active, with lithosols widespread in pediment areas. Altogether the zonal low-land type can be described as a non-calcic, arid brown soil (Non-calcic Burozem).[23] It appears to be widely associated with the thorn savanna of the better-drained Omo and Rudolf lowlands, and the frequency of truncated profiles or raw mineral soils indicates

---

[20]D'Hoore's (1964) designation of "mineral hydromorphic soils" for the upland plains of the Lower Omo Basin is quite inappropriate, while the delta plain has no "organic hydromorphic soils."

[21]See the Munsell Soil Color Charts, Munsell Color Co., Baltimore, 1954.

[22]Described as "undifferentiated vertisols of topographic depressions" by D'Hoore (1964); misleadingly called "chernozemic" soils by Schokalskaja (1953: 265).

[23]The "brown soils of arid to semiarid tropical regions" of D'Hoore (1964); inaccurately referred to as Kastanozems by Schokalskaja (1953: 265).

that "accelerated" soil stripping and local gullying is "normal" in response to overgrazing and burning.

(c) The peripheral highlands of the Lower Omo Basin are more often than not characterized by lithosols.[24] At the same time vestiges of a former cover of reddish brown (5 YR hues), loamy soils appear to be almost ubiquitous. These take the form of reworked veneers (5-10cm thick) on lag-strewn uplands or as a heterogeneous matrix to talus sheets and slope wash. Recent humification has darkened these (relict?) soils, and non-calcic, alkaline, brown (7.5 YR hues) silt loams are characteristic. The denudation of the soils of the mesic savanna is clear enough, but whether recent burning, grazing and other forms of deforestation are responsible is a matter of opinion. On the basis of aerial surveys, deep, reddish soils are indicated on more expansive upland surfaces with denser vegetation; they are probably relict.

(d) The plateau soils of the higher Omo Basin (above perhaps 1500m) must be inferred by analogy with other parts of the Ethiopian Plateau and from the brief but useful observations of Logan (1946: 16ff.). Depending on the topography, and to a lesser extent on variations of the volcanic parent material, these may be Vertisols[25] or Ferrisols (see D'Hoore, 1964). The Vertisols (Amharic woleka) of the upper Blue Nile Basin have been well described by Semmel (1964) and provide a model for soils of this type that cover about 10 million hectares of upland Ethiopia (see Dudal, 1965: 8), where they are found primarily on valley floors and seasonally-flooded intermontane plains. Vertisols are marked by dark grayish brown (10 YR-2.5 Y hues) A-horizons that may be 70 to 180 centimeters deep, resting on a dense, whitish zone of decomposing basalt. In the dry state, crack networks penetrate to a depth of 80 centimeters, whereas the soil is swollen and impermeable when wet. Texture is a silty clay, with at least 60% in the clay size-fraction, montmorillonite is the dominant clay mineral and the reaction is acidic (pH 5.0-5.3). By contrast, Semmel (1964) found Ferrisols (Amharic dukwa) on the interfluves and gently inclined hillslopes, where they appear to be almost exclusively associated with the montane forests, past and present (see Logan, 1946: 16f.). Ferrisols are also found on all acidic intrusives. Such soils have shallow (15cm), brown (7.5 YR hues) A-horizons over thick (1-3m) B-horizons of silty clay (60% in the clay fraction)--almost exclusively kaolinite, with little or no evidence of eluviation, a pH of 3.8 to 4.2 and a reddish-brown to yellowish-red color (5 YR hues (see Semmel, 1964). A meter or so of BC-horizon, with white-mottled, partly-decomposed basalt underlies the B. These mature ferrisols tend in the direction of a red-

---

[24] Include the "rocks and rock debris rich in ferromagnesian minerals" and "lithosols and lithic soils on lava" of D'Hoore (1964).

[25] More precisely described as dark lithomorphic soils with non-kaolinitic clays developed on basic igneous rocks (see D'Hoore, 1964).

yellow podsolic or <u>Rotlehm</u>[26] (in the sense of Kubiena, 1953: 273ff.), and are complemented by dark, humic intermediate soils of <u>Braunlehm</u> type on younger, well-drained surfaces, including major stream levees. Such soils are dark to strong brown (7.5 YR hues)
in color, with kaolinitic clays and <u>p</u>H values of 4.7 to 5.5 (see Semmel, 1964). Further,
Braunlehms appear to replace Rotlehms on the humid uplands of western Ethiopia (Logan,
1946: 17).

The plateau soils are of primary interest to this study since they provide the bulk
of the Omo sediment. To understand the dynamics of contemporary soil development and
geomorphic processes the writer studied conditions near Addis Ababa and in the adjacent
Ethiopian Rift at the height of the rainy season in 1967. The resulting model (see Fig. 1-7)
may be of wider applicability to the origin of both the Nile and Omo flood silts. The basic
topographic elements consist of rolling plains and lowland flats, studded with steep-sided
hills or low mountains of butte (<u>ambas</u>) or mesaform. Commonly consisting of resistant
plugs or small laccoliths, mainly of more acidic intrusives, these hills have subangular
crests, steep or near-vertical midslopes, with smooth but distinct, i.e. subrounded,
inflexions in the footslope region (<u>ca</u>. 20-30°). Surprisingly, almost all slopes of less
than 30 or 35° are covered with a deep mantle of soil, colluvium or fill; regolith or bed-
rock is rarely exposed, and then only at a local scale. The depth of solum probably averages in excess of 1 to 2 meters and where colluvial processes and mass movements are
well advanced, there may be 5 meters or so of soil sediment on lower hillslopes.

Erosional processes in the Addis Ababa region can be categorized as follows:

(i) Sheet wash. Important on all cultivated surfaces, but B or C horizons are only
rarely exposed.

(ii) Rill wash. Mainly restricted to convex slope inflexions (see Fig. 1-7), with
master-rills confined to steeper midslopes.

(iii) Gullying. Gullies dissect the fill along all significant drainage channels, cutting back from major channels in meandering lines with a depth of 1 to 2 meters.

(iv) Mass movements. Slump scarplets are conspicuous on all hillslopes exceeding
15 or 20°, indicating significant mass transfer favored by deep soil mantles, abundant
water and overintensive land use. More rapid movements include local earthflows on midslopes and rather common soilfalls along gullies and stream channels.
In combination with these denudational forces, stream dynamism is quite vigorous as can
be inferred by the rapid-moving, turbid flood waters, even at half-bankfull stage. The
major, perennial streams meander across broad, flat floodplains of laminated flood silts.

---

[26]Incorrectly given as Roterde by Schokalskaja (1953: 264); there seem to be no true
latosols on the Ethiopian Plateau. D'Hoore (1964) classifies all the red and brown clays
and loams of the plateau as "humic Ferrisols."

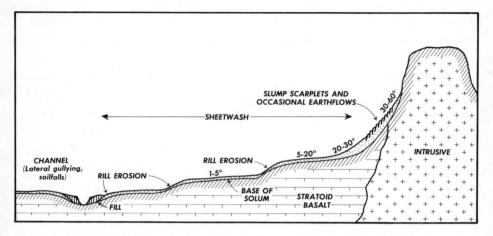

Fig. 1-7. A Model of Soil Erosion in relation to Topography near Addis Ababa (not to scale)

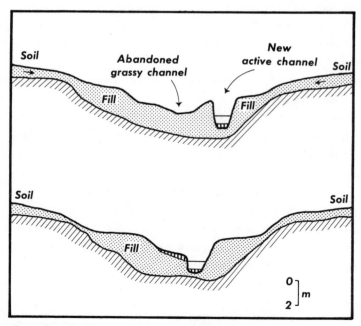

Fig. 1-8. Examples of Fill Forms in Low-Order Streams near Addis Ababa (not to scale)

The more seasonal, often intermittent tributaries have shallow, braided channels with limited alluvium although the beds are strewn with blocks and cobbles. Particularly interesting are the low-order tributaries which are developed in several generations of fine alluvium, suggesting several, recent cut-and-fill cycles in some instances or, more commonly, the shifting, rapidly meandering channels indicated by unpaired silt terraces (Fig. 1-8). Here, too, laminated flood or embanked silts are characteristic, although colluvial and bed-load components can be seen in such fill sections. Bank-undermining and bank-accretion appear to be common mechanisms.

All in all, it appears that the materials carried by the Omo flood waters are produced in the Ethiopian highlands by sheetwash, accelerated forms of mass movement, and stream erosion that primarily attack the dark topsoil of deep residual mantles. The combination of high available relief and heavy, protracted rains lends exceptional energy to fluvial processes. This would be so with an undisturbed vegetation but is even more the case in view of the thorough and almost ubiquitous human disturbance. In fact, only the intensity of chemical weathering maintains a deep residual mantle, so that the Omo River is primarily supplied with suspended rather than bed-load sediments. It appears that the Vertisols and some of the fresher, humic Ferrisols contribute the major part of this load. This can be inferred directly from the clay minerals now deposited by the Omo--montmorillonite with only a little kaolinite; it is further suggested by the dominance of rather weak elements among the heavy minerals, namely hornblende, pyroxenes and biotite that are presumably provided by fresh weathering of basaltic rocks. Altogether it seems that accelerated erosion of montmorillonitic soils from the rolling plateau surface provides the bulk of the sediments.

Climate and Hydrography of the Omo Basin

Climatography. The broad outlines of rainfall distribution and seasonal regimes are presently understood thanks to a new network of climatic stations set up in western and southern Ethiopia by the Ethiopian National Climatological Service since 1952,[27] and in Turkana by the East African Meteorological Department since 1949. The best available records are summarized in Table 1-3 (see Fig. 1-2). Almost all are incomplete, with individual months or years missing, so that yearly means were obtained by summing the averages of each set of monthly values.

Mean annual rainfall clearly increases from the shores of Lake Rudolf, with some 350 millimeters (14 in), to the Ethiopian Plateau, where precipitation ranges from 1500 to

---

[27] The brief Italian records of Jimma and Bonga 1938-40, presented in detail by Fantoli (1965: 157ff., 404ff.), are interesting but cannot be standardized with those of the new Ethiopian stations.

TABLE 1-3

MEAN MONTHLY RAINFALL TOTALS FROM AVAILABLE STATIONS, OMO BASIN
(in millimeters)

	Jan.	Feb.	Mar.	Apr.	May	June	July	Aug.	Sept.	Oct.	Nov.	Dec.	Year
Lokitaung (730m, 4°15'N, 35°45'E, 1933-1970, 35 yr)	12	23	54	122	50	19	31	13	6	14	41	26	409*
Todenyang (approx. 380m, 4°32'N, 35°55'E, 1949-1970, 18 yr)	13	25	61	81	56	10	27	10	5	11	42	20	360
Ileret (approx. 380m, 4°18'N, 36°14'E, 1957-1970, 14 yr)	20	10	39	61	37	12	12	5	0	14	67	32	308
Lokomarinyang (approx. 460m, 5°02'N, 35°38'E, 1959-1970, 11 yr)	24	21	88	109	57	15	23	11	7	36	77	20	480
Bako Mission (approx. 1980m, 5°49'N, 36°38'E, 1953-1967, 12 yr)	16	79	138	195	98	151	141	149	129	119	122	43	1381
Maji (approx. 2260m, 6°10'N, 35°35'E, 1952-1970, 13 yr)	62	90	184	233	182	126	153	162	115	131	132	84	1653
Wush Wush (1950m, 7°16'N, 36°11'E, 1954-1970, 17 yr)	53	75	144	184	234	213	202	222	222	195	86	58	1888
Bonga (1650m, 7°15'N, 36°15'E, 1953-1967, 14 yr)	48	72	151	199	225	210	179	183	196	147	88	65	1762
Jimma Airport (1680m, 7°39'N, 36°49'E, 1953-1970, 16 yr)	37	63	99	153	145	228	217	218	182	86	52	34	1513

Station													
Saja (2100m, 7°45'N, 37°22'E, 1952–1967, 14 yr)	36	38	109	130	108	209	254	241	225	94	47	35	1845
Hosseina Mission (approx. 2130m, 7°33'N, 37°52'E, 1953–1967, 12 yr)	36	30	98	169	113	130	166	188	163	65	26	28	1211
Ghion–Woliso (approx. 2050m, 8°32'N, 37°58'E, 1955–1961, 6 yr)	22	13	58	81	71	174	256	328	75	33	0	1	664

*Discrepancies of annual totals are due to rounding of monthly values presented.

26

2000 millimeters (60-80 in) (see Table 1-3). Todenyang, with 360 millimeters, is probably representative for the Omo delta plain, while Lokomarinyang, with 480 millimeters,
appears to represent the upland plains of the Lower Omo Basin; however, year-to-year
variability is very great as is the concentration of the rains in the several rainy spells
within the year. Rainfall seems to increase rapidly between 800 and 1200 meters elevation,
and areal variations beyond that altitude is in good measure a reflection of exposure and
other orographic conditions.

Three seasonal patterns emerge, despite the considerable variance from year to
year. South of about 5° 30'N (e.g. Lokitaung, Todenyang, and Lokomarinyang) there is
a double maximum in April (primary) and November (secondary), complemented by a
minor, tertiary maximum in July.[28] This pattern applies to northern Turkana and the
lowermost Omo country, and appears to be transitional between the classic equinoctial
rains of the Uganda escarpment and southern Turkana on the one hand, and the zenithal
rains of the Ethiopian Plateau (see Tato, 1964) on the other. The mid-summer, tertiary
maximum is only sporadically represented in the annual records.[29] The peripheral highlands enjoy a triple maximum in April (primary), August (secondary), and October or
November (tertiary). This is a modified form of the Ethiopian "summer" rains, and is
well represented by Bako and Maji. Finally the western part of the Ethiopian high country
has a broad maximum extending from mid-March to late November, with three superimposed peaks in April or early May, in July or August, and in late November (see Suzuki,
1967). The last of these peaks is very minor, and rather unreliable. The delimitation of
the peripheral and the interior highland types is very gradual, with Wush Wush or Bonga
intermediate between Maji and Jimma.

---

[28] According to Atiko Akiru, an exceptionally reliable informant from Namuruputh,
and the Rev. J. R. Swart of the Kaalam Mission, the rainy season begins in March or
April, usually continuing through the month of May. April has the heaviest rains and June
is already dry. The rains begin in the high country to the northwest and, a little later, to
the northeast. These impressions are of course verified by the records of Lokitaung,
Todenyang, Ileret, and Lokomarinyang, and find further confirmation in the observations
of Höhnel (1894: 146ff., 175f., 201) during April and early May of 1888, of Neumann (1898:
333f.) during March or April of 1896, of Bulatovich (1900) during March of 1898, of Harrison (1901) during late March of 1900, of Austin (1902) during mid-April of 1901, of
Bourg de Bozas (1903) during May of 1902, and of Athill (1920) during late April of 1919.
Autumn rains, if any, may come at any time between October and December, although they
are light and quite unreliable. According to Atiko Akiru, during dry years there will be no
rain from one April to the next. Somewhat fortuitously, no travellers have reported rain
during the autumn months, although the Böttego Expedition experienced 3 very light rains
and noted 4 thunderstorms in the high country during September of 1896 (Vannutelli and
Citerni, 1899: 569ff.). The same group also experienced a wet August in the Lower Omo
Basin, with 13 rainy days and only 5 days of sunny weather.

[29] Basic data supplied by Mr. Godana Tuni, Chief of the Ethiopian National Climatological Service, and by the East African Meteorological Department.

The majority of the upland rains occur as showers, preferentially in the afternoon. However at the onset and close of the "Big Rains" of mid-summer there may be continuous rains over several days (Suzuki, 1967). Lowland rainfalls appear to come mainly in the form of brief, intense thundershowers, commonly at night, or as erratic, light rains associated with protracted disturbed weather that brings thundershowers to the peripheral highlands.[30]

Relatively little is known about the thermal climate of the Omo Basin except that daily ranges exceed annual ranges, and that temperatures tend to decrease with elevation. The available data (Jackson, 1961; British Meteorological Office, 1958; Table 1-4) suggest that mean annual temperatures drop from 25 to 29°C in the lowlands to 15 to 20°C on the uplands, with even lower temperatures to be expected on the highest ranges, where frost is probably common. By interpolation it can be inferred that the low country, below 1200m or so, has a megathermal climate in the Thornthwaite classification (see Thornthwaite and Mather, 1955), the uplands a mesothermal climate (see Fig. 1-6C). By the Köppen method the comparable A/C thermal boundary (mean temperature of coolest month 18°C) would be expected near 1700 meters elevation.

Such information as there is suggests that July and August are the coolest months in the lowlands, but diurnal temperature variation is greatest in January and February. Whereas annual ranges are in the order of only 2 or 3°C, mean daily ranges vary from 9 to 12°C between July and January. The single temperature series from the Omo Delta is an incomplete, 1-year record from the Kaalam Mission (Table 1-5).[31] Standardization of

---

[30] The Chicago Expedition measured 80mm of rain from several nocturnal thunderstorms during July 1967, while Todenyang received 299mm. However rains during July and August, 1968-69, were negligible at all local stations except Lokomarinyang (8mm, August 1969).

[31] There are brief records from the Bòttego and Bourg de Bozas Expeditions. The Italians measured temperatures fairly regularly from Sept. 1 to Oct. 3, 1896, at a camp site just east of the modern Omo Delta, obtaining a mean daily maximum of 37.3, minimum of 25.0 and a mean of 31.2°C (Vannutelli and Citerni, 1899: 549f., 559f.). The French took records at several widely dispersed sites in May and June of 1902, obtaining a less homogeneous mean daily maximum of 33.5, minimum of 21.5, and mean of 27.5°C (Bourg de Bozas, 1903). Particularly valuable is the 4-month systematic record of Modha (1967) from Central Island (4°3'N, 36°2'E):

	Minimum		Maximum	
	Mean	Range	Mean	Range
January 1966	26.7°C	26.0-28.8	40.4°C	39.4-42.2
February 1966	25.6	23.3-27.2	37.0	31.7-42.2
March 1966	26.2	25.0-26.7	38.7	31.1-41.7
April 1966	25.1	22.8-28.3	35.6	27.7-42.2

Finally, the Chicago Expedition recorded temperatures at a site on the upland plain northwest of the Delta from June 25 to August 31, 1968. The results are presented in Appendix A.

TABLE 1-4

MEAN MONTHLY TEMPERATURES FROM SELECTED STATIONS, OMO BASIN

(in °C)

	Jan.	Feb.	Mar.	Apr.	May	June	July	Aug.	Sept.	Oct.	Nov.	Dec.	Year
Lokitaung (730m, 1945-1954, 10 yr)													
Max.	33.4	33.9	33.6	31.0	31.1	31.4	30.8	30.6	31.8	32.0	32.0	32.1	32.0
Min.	22.4	22.9	23.0	21.3	22.1	21.9	21.3	21.2	22.0	21.9	21.9	22.1	22.0
Mean	27.9	28.4	28.3	26.2	26.6	26.7	26.1	25.9	26.9	27.0	27.0	27.1	27.0
Bako Mission (1980m, 1954-1962, 7 yr)													
Max.	22.2	25.3*	22.4	22.1	21.6	20.5	19.9	19.9	21.1	21.5	22.3	22.7	21.8
Min.	10.6	10.4	11.9	11.9	11.9	10.9	10.4	10.4	10.7	11.0	10.7	10.4	10.9
Mean	16.4	18.1*	17.2	17.0	16.8	15.7	15.2	15.2	15.9	16.3	16.5	16.6	16.4
Bonga (1650m, 1953-1968, 16 yr)													
Max.	29.6	30.3	29.9	28.6	28.2	26.3	24.8	25.1	26.2	28.3	28.4	28.7	27.9
Min.	10.0	11.0	11.8	12.7	12.5	12.5	12.4	12.6	11.8	10.4	10.4	10.0	11.7
Mean	19.8	20.7	20.8	20.7	20.4	19.4	18.6	18.9	19.0	19.4	19.4	19.4	19.7
Jimma Airport (1680m, 1952-1968, 15 yr)													
Max.	29.1	28.7	29.3	28.3	27.7	25.6	23.8	24.0	25.6	26.6	27.3	27.8	26.8
Min.	6.2	9.5	10.6	11.7	12.0	12.2	13.0	13.0	12.7	10.7	8.5	6.8	10.5
Mean	17.7	19.1	20.0	20.0	19.9	18.9	18.4	18.5	19.2	18.7	17.9	17.3	18.7

*Dubious records.

TABLE 1-5

TEMPERATURE AND RAINFALL AT KAALAM MISSION,
JUNE 1966-MAY 1967
(Recorded by J. R. Swart)

	Mean Maxima	No. of Observations	Mean Minima	No. of Observations	Mean °C	Range °C	Rainfall (mm.)
June (1966)	32.5	11	27.8*	11	30.1[t]	4.7	–
July	33.5	31	26.2*	31	29.9[t]	7.3	1.0
August	33.6	30	23.7	30	28.7	9.9	65.5
September	34.3[t]	18	22.6[t]	27	28.5[t]	11.7	34.5[t]
October	33.2[t]	3	24.2[t]	3	28.7[t]	9.0	–
November	33.0	23	21.4	24	27.2	11.6	31.0
December	34.7[t]	28	20.7[t]	30	27.7[t]	14.0	–
January (1967)	35.0[t]	9	19.8[t]	10	27.4[t]	15.3	9.0[t]
February	34.9	22	22.6	22	28.7	12.3	1.0[t]
March	36.2	26	22.7	26	29.5	13.5	73.5[t]
April	34.3	6	21.3	6	27.8	13.0	8.0[t]
May	31.9	25	20.8	26	26.4	11.1	107.5
Average	33.9	232	22.8[t]	246	28.4	11.1	330.5[t]

*Incorrect exposure indicated.

[t] Data not fully representative.

these readings with Lokitaung, via Lodwar, indicates that the Lokitaung temperature record (Table 1-4) is representative of the delta plain but about 1°C lower.

In the high country, diurnal ranges increase with elevation and latitude. The annual range does not increase, but daily minimum temperatures in December, January and February drop so low in basins subject to inversions that December is the coolest month at Jimma (see Table 1-4), although the peak of the rainy season (July or August) brings the lowest monthly means elsewhere on the plateau.

Unfortunately there is little or no systematic information on relative humidity,[32] evaporation, or wind speeds and directions. However, there can be little question that southerly winds, from a SSW to ESE quadrant, are the rule at all seasons both over Lake Rudolf and the Omo delta plain.[33]

---

[32] Relative humidities were determined for 8 years (1947-54) at Lokitaung, averaging 67% at 8 AM and 51% at 2 PM for the year. The least humid month is January (58 and 46% respectively), the most humid April (74 and 57% respectively) (British Meteorological Office, 1958). For the Chicago observations of 1968, see Appendix A.

[33] According to Fuchs (1935) N or NE winds are significant at the northern end of Lake Rudolf during March and April, at which time they are supposed to usher in the rainy season. This is not supported by Höhnel's (1890, 1894) observations at that time of year and was emphatically denied by local informants. Possibly Fuchs was referring to the wind shifts that commonly accompany thunderstorms or to diurnal lake breezes. The

Synthesizing the preceding materials on a Thornthwaite moisture-balance,[34] the

Lower Omo Basin has an arid megathermal climate (EA'd), with no water surplus at any

time (Fig. 1-9). The Ethiopian plateau, on the other hand, enjoys a humid mesothermal

climate (BB'r), with little or no water deficiency (Fig. 1-10). By the Köppen system, the

BW/BS boundary in the Omo lowlands lies near the 390-millimeter isohyet. Consequently

the delta plain has an arid tropical climate (BWhw'), the adjacent higher plains the semi-

arid counterpart (BShw'), both with a double rainfall maximum. Similarly, the highlands

would be classified as summer-moist subtropical (Cwi), with little annual temperature

variation.

Climatology. A discussion of the dynamic climatology of the Omo Basin is ham-

pered by the inadequacies that plague tropical meteorology as well as by the paucity of

upper air data from East Africa. Nonetheless it is important to derive at least a tentative

understanding of circulation and weather patterns if the rainy and dry seasons are to be

analyzed in connection with recent fluctuations of Lake Rudolf.

"northerly trades" that Smith (1900) found dominant in the Usno valley during December
and January may have been a diurnal mountain wind, blowing downvalley. Vannutelli and
Citerni (1899: 562, 564f.) made a fair number of observations of northerly or northeasterly winds in late July and August, 1896, while travelling down the Omo River from latitude 6°30' to the Delta; these were, however, primarily attributed to local orographic
factors. In fact, Nowack (1954: 25ff.), who kept a useful weather record in the Konso
country (northeast of Lake Stefanie) during February and March of 1938, demonstrated the
existence of a light to moderate mountain wind, blowing from the north in a longitudinally-
oriented valley during the evening and night hours. The Chicago Camp observations from
late June through August of 1968 include only 8 incidents of northerly wind components
from a total of 174 observations (see Appendix A). This is complemented by the record of
Vannutelli and Citerni (1899: 564) from the northeast corner of Lake Rudolf during September of 1896. Of 107 wind observations, 43 were from the SE, 27 SW, 22 S, 10 E, 2 NE
and only 1 N. However, a diurnal cycle of winds has been repeatedly indicated from the
windward shores of Lake Rudolf, although its exact nature remains controversial. The
Chicago observations from northeast of Lokitaung, near the base of Mt. Laburr, noted
only southerly or easterly wind components at 7 AM and 2 PM from June 11-21, 1968. However, 5 of the 11 recordings at 9 PM refer to northerly or northwesterly winds (see Appendix A). Beadle (1932a), basing himself on almost 7 weeks of observations on the northwestern shore of Lake Rudolf during the winter of 1930-31, described the following daily
rhythm: a very predictable SE wind rising at 9 AM, reaching maximum intensity at 3 PM,
and then veering to NE. Calm prevailed after dark. However, Fuchs (1935), who worked
in the same area at the same season, claimed strong winds in the mornings until 11 AM,
followed by a dead calm from 1 or 2 PM to 4 PM, after which a regular, light northerly
wind preceded SE or SSE winds that blew strong during the evening and night. The general
wind observations of Modha (1967), made on Central Island between August, 1965, and February, 1966, indicated that days were generally calm, with southeasterly winds during the
nights, beginning to blow between 7 and 11 PM. Interestingly, Modha also noted that a
northerly or northwesterly wind sometimes came up during the day.

[34] Apart from the necessarily arbitrary nature of all climatic classifications, the
Thornthwaite system has not proved to be particularly successful in lower latitudes and it
is doubtful whether it represents a true water balance for the study area. Similar reserva-
tions are in order for the runoff estimates given further below.

31

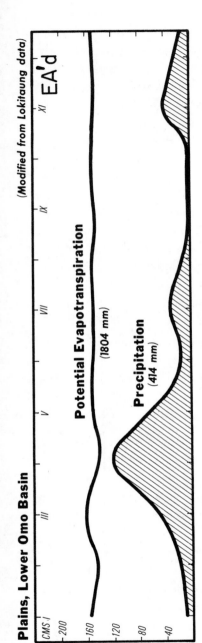

Fig. 1-9. Annual Water–Balance for the "Upland" Plains of the Lower Omo Basin, after the Thornthwaite–Mather method. Station data from Lokitaung, adding 1° C to the monthly temperature values.

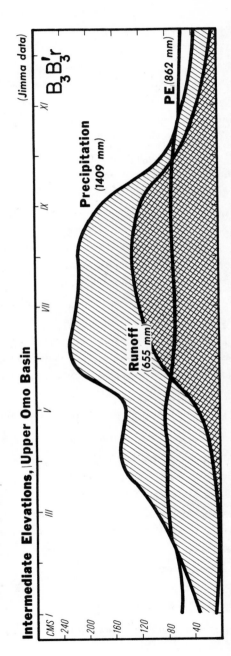

Fig. 1-10. Annual Water–Balance for the Upper Omo Basin. Station data from Jimma (1680m).

The dynamics of the climate of Ethiopia, although poorly understood, seem to hinge on the recognition of diverse though distinctive airmasses as well as the presence of divisions or discontinuities in both the pressure and moisture fields. Despite the complexity of airstream interaction over the region during different climatic seasons, some evidence has been provided that accords with general theoretical approaches to tropical climatology. Weickmann (1964), for example, has noted that the relatively permanent and stable system anchored by the highland mass of Ethiopia establishes recognizable discontinuities with the more transient air flows. Such discontinuities are identified either as zones of convergence, usually involving surface flow, or as a distinctive pressure trough. One such discontinuity is significantly located between the elevated highlands of north-central Ethiopia and the lower-lying water expanse of Lake Victoria. This discontinuity emphasizes the orographic influence on the dynamic system. Westerly wind components dominate west of this meridional discontinuity, with advection of westerly moisture over the Congo Basin, while easterly components with moisture from the Indian Ocean are found to the east.

Another type of discontinuity has been identified for a single year, 1964, by Suzuki (1967) in the form of moisture content. Such moisture discontinuities were observed to shift in some accordance with pressure patterns of the wet and dry seasons. Although one year is insufficient to permit firm generalizations, this method did demonstrate that rational patterns can be sought to explain the march of rainfall seasons and their associated weather.

In order to obtain a more systematic appreciation of discontinuities and airstreams a set of 6 monthly maps (Fig. 1-11) was constructed, using Weickmann (1963), Thompson (1965), Suzuki (1967), Osman and Hastenrath (1969), and the U.S. Weather Bureau (1965-70) Synoptic Weather Maps since 1960. The resulting maps (Fig. 1-11) are not more than an approximation, but they do allow some generalizations about airstreams and dominant airmasses.

January. Northeasterly airstreams of continental tropical (cT) and modified continental polar (cP) air associated with the Siberian anticyclonic circulation invade northeastern Africa, one branch sweeping through the Sudan to the rim of the Congo Basin, the other crossing Somalia and Kenya into Tanzania. These branches diverge to the north and converge to the south of Ethiopia, creating a zone of cyclonic wind shear over the plateau. Maritime tropical air of Atlantic and Congo origin (mTa) is drawn in from the west into the zone of convergence, bringing rains to Uganda and western Tanzania. This is the major dry season in northern East Africa, lasting from early December to early March and bringing clear, dry and stable air to the Ethiopian Plateau. The northeasterlies diverge over Somalia and recurve into the Rudolf area as strong, persistent southeasterly winds.

March. The northeast "monsoon" winds are replaced by two anticyclonic circulations, one over the Sahara, the other over the Arabian Sea. mTa airstreams shift into the southern Sudan and western Ethiopia as the Saharan circulation weakens, while maritime tropical air of Indian Ocean origin (mTi) is advected into Kenya and southern Ethiopia by the high

33

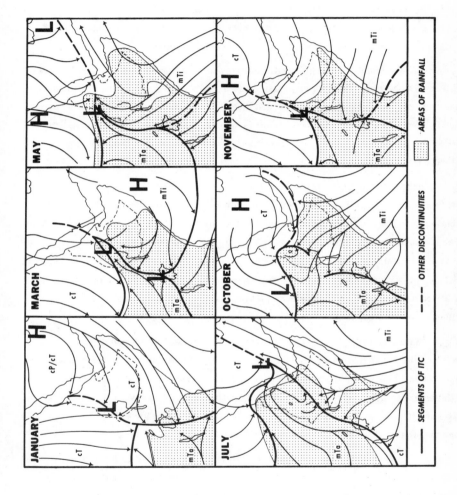

Fig. 1-11. Seasonal Changes of Circulation Patterns over East Africa

pressure cell just east of Somalia. Convergence of the airstreams maintains semi-permanent lows over both the Ethiopian Plateau and Lake Victoria, with a tendency to divergence and subsidence over the Rudolf area. In this way the major rainy season begins in the equatorial belt and southwestern Ethiopia. Much of the rainfall is related to potential instability, although both zones and periods of bad weather can often be recognized. In part these take the form of "surges" in the easterly stream of mTi air, possibly initiated by incursions of Antarctic air at high levels into the Indian Ocean. In part they occur as mysterious "cloud lines" in the westerly mTa air. Finally, they may also be related to upper air troughs in the northern hemisphere westerlies.[35]

May. A trough extending from the Asiatic low across Arabia promotes a northerly flow of dry air across northern Ethiopia and much of the Sudan, while inducing the southeast trades from the Indian Ocean to recurve and diverge over southern Ethiopia and Somalia. General convergence on the high plateau draws in moist airstreams over western Ethiopia, but divergence of the southerly mTi airstream favors a brief dry spell over central Ethiopia during late May.

July. Intensification of the Asiatic low by mid-summer draws in a strong southwesterly airstream over northern Ethiopia, with local eddies over the uplands and with a marked discontinuity to the recurving Indian Ocean airstreams across the Ethiopian Rift. Disturbances and potential instability in the westerly mTa airmass provide the Big Rains of mid-June to mid-September, while the advance and retreat of the associated airmass discontinuities bring periods of almost continual rain (see Suzuki, 1967). There is less rain in the mTi air east of the Rift, primarily due to divergent flow, with subsidence of dry air over the Rudolf area and Somalia.

October. With high pressures reestablished over southwestern Asia and dropping pressures over the Indian and South Atlantic Oceans, a dry northeasterly airstream advances into northern Ethiopia and the central Sudan. A semi-permanent low is centered just west of Ethiopia, with mTa and mTi airstreams competing at different levels over the western plateau and the southern Sudan where the rains continue. A southerly flow of mTi air brings precipitation to Somalia and southern Ethiopia.

November. As pressures rise over the northern Indian Ocean, the southeast trades disappear from East Africa. Instead, Kenya, Somalia and southern Ethiopia receive rains from mTi air advected from the east, while the rainy season in western Ethiopia and the southern Sudan concludes with the disappearance of the easterly jet in the upper tropo-

---

[35]See Riehl (1954: chap. 12-14), Trewartha (1961: chap. 8-9), Flohn (1965), Flohn and Fraedrich (1966), and Gichuiya (1971), for insights into the problem of tropical disturbances.

sphere (Osman and Hastenrath, 1969). By mid-December the winter circulation with $\underline{cT}$ air has been reestablished.

Hydrographic Data. No systematic observations on the hydrology of the Omo River or Lake Rudolf exist, and information is limited to the subjective impressions of passing travellers or local informants. Consequently the Thornthwaite-Mather (1955) water balance and runoff computations are of considerable--although qualified--value in assessing discharge periods and maxima.

There is no water surplus anywhere in the Lower Omo Basin according to the Thornthwaite-Mather water balance (see Fig. 1-9)[36] and, accordingly, there should be no runoff. This is not quite so, however. Minor watercourses descending from the uplands or draining dissected areas of even limited relief carry water after heavy rains. This run-off is quite insignificant for the hydrological budget of the Omo River. But it does promote local gullying or fan activity, and periodically cleans out the flood silts that accumulate within the mouths of channels tributary to the Omo floodplain.

For the highlands peripheral to the Lower Omo Basin the situation is different. Thornthwaite-Mather budgets were calculated employing the precipitation data of Maji and Bako with temperature means intermediate between those of Jimma and Lokitaung (Figs. 1-12 and 1-13). These parameters should be representative of the major catchment of the Kibish and Usno rivers respectively. For the Kibish, it indicates runoff and discharge throughout the year, with maxima in May and August (Fig. 1-12). In actual practice, the lower Kibish carries water as far as Nakwa for many months each spring and summer, and occasionally flows all year.[37] The Usno flow should last from June through March, with a maximum in August (Fig. 1-13).[38]

---

[36] Fig. 12 employs the precipitation data of Lokitaung, but 1° C has been added to each monthly temperature mean.

[37] As in 1917, according to Worthington (1932). Maximum discharge usually takes place during April and May, in response to local rains (Atiko Akiru, personal communication). Bankfull or overbank discharge occurred during May or early June of 1968 in the Kibish and other streams west of Nakwa, probably one of the wettest springs in memory. Lokomarinyang received 409mm precipitation during March of that year, 246 during April, 226 during May, and none during the next 4 months. At Maji, both April and May were much wetter than average, with 313 and 239mm precipitation respectively.

[38] No local information was obtained for the Usno but, at least during wet years, discharge commences earlier in the year. Our helicopter reconnaissance showed the Usno at or near bankfull stage during early July of both 1968 and 1969, and locally at overbank stage during August of 1967 and 1968. The Bòttego Expedition was only able to cross the Usno with difficulty in mid-August of 1896, due to the swift current, although the depth was only about 1.5m (Vannutelli and Citerni, 1899: 327). Smith (1896) made comparable observations in late July, 1895. In late May of 1902, Bourg de Bozas (1903) found a shallow stream with a weak current.

36

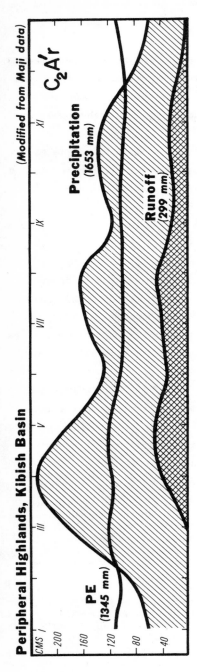

Fig. 1-12. Annual Water-Balance for the Kibish Basin. Precipitation data from Maji (2260m).

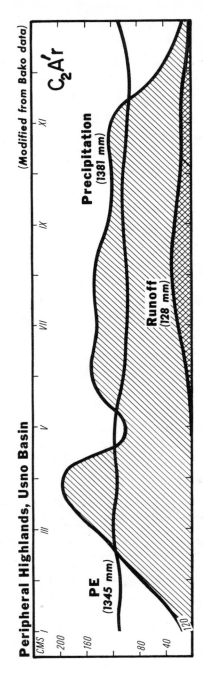

Fig. 1-13. Annual Water-Balance for the Usno Basin. Precipitation data from Bako (1980m).

The Omo River clearly responds to the runoff regime calculated for the middle and upper drainage basin, based on the data from Jimma (Fig. 1-10). Precipitation exceeds potential evapotranspiration 9 months of the year, and runoff should be available all year, with maximum discharge to be expected in August. The available information[39] indicates that, in the lower Omo, discharge is small from December through April, with a minimum in March. The river begins to rise in April or May, depending on the year. It will commonly continue to rise rapidly during June, fluctuating considerably through July and August. The maximum level is reached by the end of August or early in September, and discharge decreases rapidly during late September. Flood velocities appear to be great, with Höhnel (1891) already measuring 1.8 to 2.0 km/hr during a pre-flood surge in May, and velocities of 9 to 10 km/hr estimated at the height of the annual flood in 1967.

From all indications and on the basis of rough budget approximations, most of the water of Lake Rudolf--in the order of 80 to 90%--appears to be derived from the Omo River. The Turkwell[40] and Kerio (Fig. 1-4), the only other affluents of any significance, are dry in their lower courses for most of the year (Champion, 1937); their relative contribution in terms of discharge and seepage may be about equal. Consequently the seasonal and longer-term fluctuations of Rudolf level must in large part be controlled by the duration and intensity of the rainy season in highland Ethiopia. In addition to this rainfall factor, evaporation over the lake itself must also effect the hydrologic budget. Mean temperatures and wind speeds appear to change little from year to year but cloud cover is susceptible to a considerable degree of variability.

The hydrologic regime of Lake Rudolf can be inferred from the scattered gauge readings taken at Ferguson's Gulf since 1949. For a total of approximately 10 years, monthly levels of the lake can be safely reconstructed by interpolation from 247 readings between 1949 and 1961 (Fig. 1-14). Unfortunately the fragmentary record since 1966

---

[39]Atiko Akiru and J. R. Swart personal communication; confirmed by the observations of F. H. Brown and the Chicago group, September-October, 1966; June-September, 1967; June-August, 1968-70. Höhnel (1894: 202ff.) gives a vivid description of the beginning of the flood during April and early May of 1888. High water during the summer months is reported by Vannutelli and Citerni (1899: chap. 12), Bourg de Bozas (1903) and Smith (1896), low water during the winter months by Wellby (1900), Harrison (1901) and Smith (1900).

[40]Gauge readings are available for the upper Turkwell catchment: (1) On the Suam, at 1°29'N, 35°00'E, since 1962; (2) On the Marun, a minor Turkwell tributary from the Cherangani Hills, at 1°33'N, 35°31'E, since 1957; and (3) On the Wei-Wei, another minor Cherangani affluent, at 1°26'N, 35°28'E, since 1962. Data supplied by the Water Development Division, Nairobi, shows one or more maxima, occurring at any time between April and October; the lowest readings were normally made in January or February. The resulting periodicity of discharge is broadly similar to that of the Omo River, in the sense that the Turkwell and Kerio would contribute water to Lake Rudolf at about the time of the Omo flood.

38

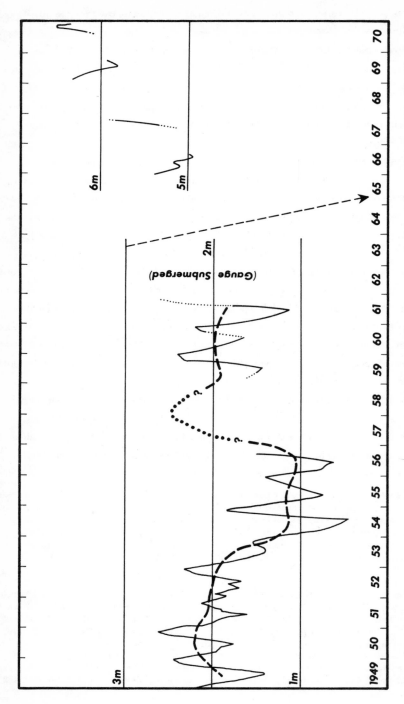

Fig. 1-14. Monthly Gauge Readings 1949–1970. Incomplete, raw data courtesy Water Development Division, Nairobi. The heavy broken line 1949–61 indicates the trend of mean annual levels. No exact calibration has been established between the 1966–70 and the 1949–61 records: the 4m displacement is approximated from the geomorphologic evidence and will require revision.

cannot be calibrated with the earlier observations since the original gauge was submerged in 1962.[41] Compensating for superimposed annual fluctuations of level, the seasonal fluctuation of level averaged 95 centimeters[42] between a maximum of 128 and a minimum of 56 centimeters. The highest annual level is reached between October and December, the lowest between May and July. Since Omo discharge continues to be added throughout the year, the total evaporative loss is well over 95 centimeters, probably closer to the 300 centimeters frequently estimated for open water surfaces in arid parts of tropical Africa. The negative annual balance of 7125×10^6 cubic meters of water is already quite appreciable and, assuming a total evaporative loss of 300 centimeters compensated for at 80% by the Omo, the discharge of that river could be estimated at 18×10^9 cubic meters or about 22% of the annual Nile discharge at Aswan. Until a gauge is installed, it is probably reasonable to assume that annual Omo discharge lies somewhere between 15 and 25×10^9 cubic meters.

---

[41]Information supplied by Mr. Alv Svaeren of the Water Development Division, Nairobi, and Mr. M. J. Mann of the F.A.O. Fisheries Research Project, Bujumbura.

[42]Considerably greater than the crude estimate of 30cm by Fuchs (1939).

CHAPTER 2

GEOMORPHOLOGY OF THE OMO DELTA PLAIN

> Ascendiamo la piccola eleva-
> zione.... a un tratto ci si pre-
> senta davanti una large distesa
> argentea di acque. Restiamo
> attoniti ad ammirare.... Da
> questo momento il gran pro-
> blema della geografia moderna
> è risoluto, il nostro sogno
> avverato. L'Omo si getta nel
> Rodolfo!
>
> --Lamberto Vannutelli, 1899

Geomorphologic Units

During the 1950's, when Lake Rudolf was low, the deltaic plain of the Omo River
had an area of about 1150 square kilometers. In a north-south direction, it measured as
much as 82 kilometers, with an average width of almost 18 kilometers.[1] The elongated,
meridional arrangement of this delta, together with its rectilinear margins, reflect on the
structural lineaments that control the northern extremity of the Rudolf trough. Within
these confines the Omo Delta can be subdivided into a number of units, defined on the basis
of criteria such as surface form, surficial sediments, genetic landforms, relative location, and the relative age of emergence of submergence. These geomorphologic units can
be identified as follows (Figs. 2-1 and 2-2).

(a) The Meander Belt[2] is part of the convex, Omo floodplain with meandering channels, with natural levees, numerous cut-off meanders, occasional ox-bow lakes or clay
plugs, and restricted flood basins. Whereas the southern and northern parts of this belt
are markedly convex, the central sector tends to be more flat, with point-bar ridges and
swales well developed. On this basis the northern or Murle and the southern or Narok

---

[1] Excluding the irregular fringe of beach ridges.

[2] Terminology in general follows that of Bernard and LeBlanc (1965) as developed
for the Mississippi Delta. The major exception is that "delta flats" is here substituted for
their "deltaic plain," a usage that would be confusing in the Omo Delta with its complex of functional and non-functional components. Instead, "delta plain" is used here in
its most general sense.

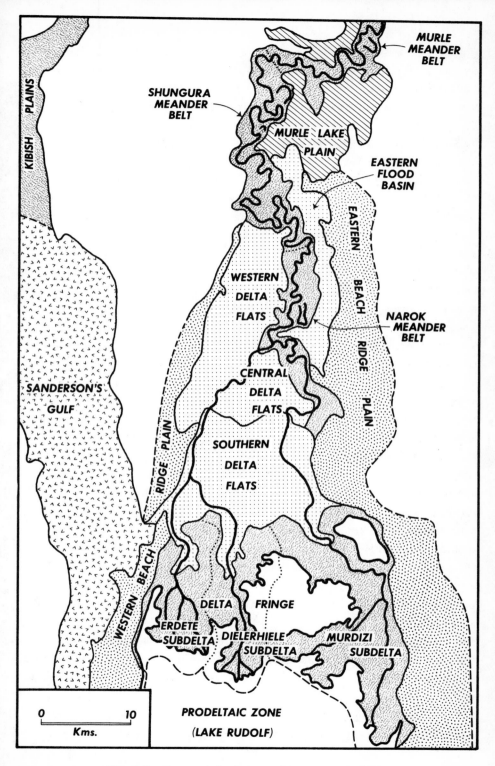

Fig. 2-1. Geomorphologic Units of the Omo Delta Plain

Meander Belts are distinguished from the central sector, the Shungura Meander Belt. A
good number of minor overflow channels and dispersal streams breach the levees wher-
ever the meander belt is accompanied by extensive alluvial flats; however, such low-lying
flood basins are generally of more complex origin and merit individual status.

(b) The Eastern Flood Basin forms the only extensive sector of alluvial flats for
the convex Meander Belt; dispersal and particularly gathering streams are well-developed
with several non-outlet depressions that serve as backswamps.

(c) The Delta Flats. The central part of the Omo Delta comprises a number of
broad, flat surfaces that currently function (at least topographically) as flood basins to the
Omo Meander Belt. Closer inspection shows that such surfaces normally consist of non-
functional interdistributary basins, lagoonal mudflats and networks of distributary channels. The distributaries today function as dispersal streams during periods of overbank
discharge, the lowlands serve as incidental flood basins, while gathering streams are well
developed where seepage from the meander belt is prominent. The Delta Flats can be subdivided into several parts: (i) The Western Delta Flats, a former delta fringe accreted by
a succession of ephemeral, multiple dispersal streams and distributaries, diverging from
the Narok Meander Belt. (ii) The Central Delta Flats, also dominated by topographically-
subdued, fossil forms as the western Delta Flats, more recently cut across by sinuous but
non-meandering distributary channels of the Omo River. (iii) The Southern Delta Flats,
consisting mainly of prodeltaic deposits, little modified by deltaic remodelling prior to
rapid and relatively recent emergence; bounded by younger Omo distributaries with limited
sinuosity.

(d) The Delta Fringe. Except for the natural levees of the Omo distributaries, the
Delta Fringe has been submerged since 1962, presenting an exaggerated birdfoot profile.
The 1957-59 air photos show that a birdfoot profile was then characteristic of the most
active or Dielerhiele Subdelta, with the deteriorating Erdete and Murdizi Subdeltas
increasingly prone to cuspate remodelling by wave and current action. At that time distributaries, natural levees, flood basins, lagoonal mudflats, interdistributary bays, distributary mouth bars, and barrier bars and spits were well developed in active deltaic
settings, with deteriorating channels notable for the older subdeltas. In the 1950's the
Delta Fringe included two large, unnamed lakes, here labelled "Nagum" and "Fadja" for
convenience.

(e) The subaquatic Prodeltaic Zone at the head of Lake Rudolf is next to unknown.
The lake waters are highly turbid for 35 to 50 kilometers or more beyond the Delta Fringe,
depending on the season; presumably flat-lying or inclined suspended sediments constitute
the lake flood here.

(f) The Beach Ridge Plains. A discontinuous belt of subparallel beach ridges,
mainly dissected or non-functional, girdles the Omo Delta. Most intact and relatively

narrow (1 km or so) are the lowest of these, found adjacent to the alluvial lowlands. Somewhat more eroded are the multiple sets of higher beach ridges found 5 kilometers and more beyond the immediate delta. Their relief, in as far as preserved, is far more prominent. Consequently, in distinguishing Eastern and Western Beach Ridge Plains it is useful to consider the discontinuous nature of these surfaces and their relative development.

(g) The Murle Lake Plain. The northern end of the delta is marked by extensive remnants of an old lake floor, fringed by beach ridges, and continuing up the Omo Valley for 25 kilometers past Lake Dipa to White Sands in the form of alluvial or fluvio-lacustrine terraces. The last are offset from the functional delta surfaces by marked terrace steps but remain well below the level of the Kibish outcrops; they can be related to the higher littoral formations of the Beach Ridge Plains.

(h) Sanderson's Gulf. Although the great synclinal depression of Sanderson's Gulf is not strictly a part of the Omo Delta, it has long functioned as a flood basin for overbank discharge or dispersal streams from the Omo River. Moving through an interridge depression just south of Fort Namuruputh, Omo waters inundate the lower-lying parts of the "Gulf" for several months every year until they evaporate. When Lake Rudolf was higher in the past, the Gulf was connected by a broad interbarrier inlet to the open lake. The broad, flat floor of the Gulf can be subdivided into a number of poorly-defined environments, bordered by a fringe of non-descript littoral deposits and poorly-developed beach ridges. To the north, the Gulf merges with the alluvial plain of the Kibish River and its delta (see Figs. 1-3 and 2-2).

The Laboratory Data

These regions and meso-environments will be described and analyzed in turn, with reference to the detailed map of Omo Delta geomorphology (Fig. 2-2), the abstraction of geomorphic units (Fig. 2-1), and the specific maps or photographs illustrating various themes. The corresponding sedimentologic data is presented in Tables B-1 and B-2 (Appendix B). Texture was determined by the hydrometer technique and wet sieving, calcium carbonate content by the Chittick gasometric apparatus, while pH values were obtained electrometrically in distilled water. The description of structural, textural and oxidation properties follows that of the U. S. Soil Survey (Smith et al., 1960), while the criteria for sorting are after Payne (1942).[3] Additional soil properties were determined for a number of selected samples (Table 2-4) by the University of Wisconsin Soils Department.

The total sample suite analyzed is, of course, far too small to provide a definitive picture of lateral and vertical facies variation from each of the geomorphic units identified.

---

[3] In general the methods employed are similar to those indicated by Butzer and Hansen (1968: Appendix A), while general terms and concepts are described by Butzer (1971b: chap. 11).

Indeed, the sediments of certain meso-environments could only be examined in the field. Nonetheless, despite some unfortunate lacunae, it is felt that the laboratory analyses are representative, and that they strongly support the field observation that there only are a limited number of distinct sediment types, that intrafacies variations are small, and that interfacies contrasts are distinctive. The suite is further complicated by the nature of those samples taken at depths of 50 centimeters, i.e. often at or near the base of the contemporary A-horizons. This selection was deliberate since it was considered of topmost priority to sample modern depositional environments--which necessarily coincide with the sphere of active pedogenesis. Those samples taken from A-horizons are indicated by an asterisk in Table B-1, and inspection shows that they do not differ appreciably in terms of basic sediment properties from samples lacking humification and biotic activity. The presence of mottling and other oxidation phenomena indicates seasonal waterlogging of the subsoil. However, the alternating reduction and oxidation implied is invariably weak and restricted, and none of these cases would merit the status of a strong gley, i.e. an Ag, Cg, or g-horizon (as defined by the U.S. Soil Survey). In fact, the millivolt readings on the sample suite were all fairly uniform and undistinctive, ranging from +110 to +220.

The Meander Belt

Geometry. The Omo River meanders through most of the Lower Omo Basin, accompanied by levees, alluvial flats and occasional point-bar sequences, cut-offs, clay plugs and backswamps. The individual characteristics of this floodplain vary from one stretch to another within the confines of the delta plain. Altogether the several segments that constitute the Meander Belt comprise an area of about 175 square kilometers. The more striking parameters of several of these segments (see Fig. 2-1) are given by Table 2-1. Meander wave lengths and amplitudes (see Morisawa, 1968: 137ff.), as well as channel widths, were obtained from the air photos and averaged for each channel segment. The index of sinuosity, defined as the ratio of channel length to valley length (Schumm, 1963), expresses the degree of sinuosity, with a meandering reach defined by an index of greater than 1.5.

The Murle Meander Belt (Fig. 2-3) is fairly representative of the lower Omo floodplain in general. The width of the alluvial tract is normally between 1 and 3 kilometers, and sinuosity approximates 1.9. However the meanders do not move freely over an active alluvial surface but are peripherally cut into older and higher deposits. Consequently the channel is relatively stable, with limited development of point-bar sequences and few cutoffs, while many stretches are almost straight. Meander length and amplitude are correspondingly variable, with average dimensions of 2.06 and 1.10 kilometers respectively, while channel width averages 380 meters and normally ranges from 320 to 420 meters.

45

TABLE 2-1

GEOMETRY OF THE OMO CHANNEL

Segment	Index of Sinuosity	Meander Length (km)	Meander Amplitude (km)	Mean Channel Width (and Range) (meters)
Murle Meander Belt	1.90	2.06	1.10	380 (320-420)
Shungura Meander Belt	2.89	2.43	1.55	278 (210-340)
Narok Meander Belt (Omo)	1.36	1.51	0.90	340 (240-360)
Narok Meander Belt (Murdizi)	1.65	1.95	1.27	172 (110-210)
Omo from Narok to Bifurcation	1.19	----	----	512 (360-680)
Erdete Subdelta	1.15	----	----	224 (175-290)
Dielerhiele Subdelta	1.14	----	----	293 (240-360)
Murdizi Subdelta	1.20	----	----	250 (160-320)

TABLE 2-2

CHANGING SINUOSITY OF THE OMO CHANNEL
SINCE EMERGENCE OF MURLE LAKE PLAIN

Segment	Stage 4 (Modern)	Stage 3	Stage 2	Stage 1
Murle Belt	1.90	2.02	2.02	1.81
Shungura Belt	2.89	3.25	2.12	1.10
Narok Belt (Omo)	1.36	2.16	2.14	1.33
Narok Belt (Murdizi)	(1.65)	1.72	1.65	----
Omo below Narok	1.19	1.14	----	----

TABLE 2-3

CHANGING MEANDER LENGTH OF THE OMO CHANNEL
SINCE EMERGENCE OF MURLE LAKE PLAIN

Segment	Stage 4	Stage 3	Stage 2	Stage 1
Murle Belt	2.06 km	2.30 km	2.30 km	2.23 km
Shungura Belt	2.43	2.45	2.84	----
Narok Belt (Omo)	1.51	1.89	2.63	----
Narok Belt (Murdizi)	(1.95)	2.10	1.86	----

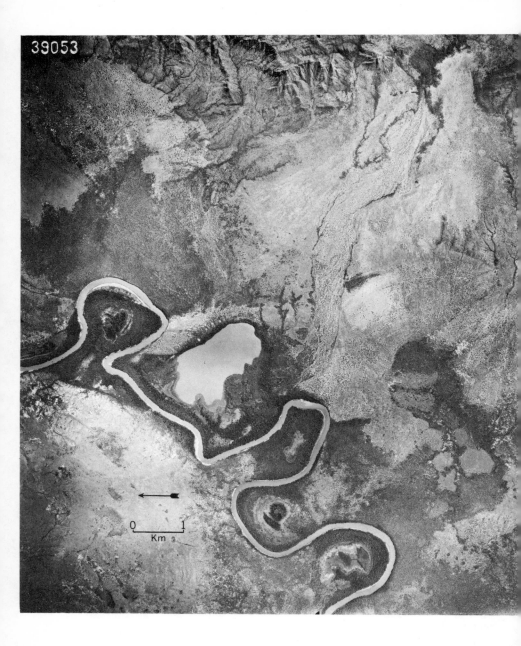

Fig. 2-3. The Murle Meander Belt and Lake Dipa. Murle Lake Plain at bottom with related beach ridges at bottom right and top. December 1967. With permission of the Ethiopian Mapping and Geography Institute (copyright).

The levees of the Murle Meander Belt are relatively low and generally rise little more than 1 to 1.5 meters above the general level of the alluvial flats. Outside channel banks in meander bends are normally undercut and many inside banks are as well. This, together with the narrow berms of flood silts (currently being accreted along the channel peripheries) indicates that the channel was incised in more recent times, with alluviation now largely restricted to the actual channel. Such a conclusion is supported by several other features: (1) The highest, fresh alluvium deposited during the 1967 and 1968 flood seasons was at least 1 to 1.5 meters lower than the general levee elevation. (2) Only limited tracts of the flood basins were flooded at the height of the 1967 and 1968 floods, and these were primarily inundated by seepage rather than overbank discharge. (3) Tributary gully systems sometimes exhibit quite recent cut-and-fill cycles. Such gullies have alluvial terraces at approximately +3 and +5 meters, the lower of which is graded to and interdigited with the alluvial flats of the recent floodplain. In other words, the tributary gullies were quite recently incised about 3 meters in response to Omo channel downcutting; a meter or so of fresh alluvium has since accumulated at the bottom of these gullies, deposits that can be traced longitudinally to the Omo banks, where they interfinger with Omo flood silts. (4) Some channel shortening has occurred in recent times with cutting off of both the Lake Dipa and, further north, the Lake Lokulat (5·22°N, 36·03°E) meanders, so that sinuosity has been reduced.

In other words, the "typical" Omo floodplain of the Murle Meander Belt is, in part, non-functional as a result of quite recent readjustments of stream equilibrium and floodplain geometry. Remodelling has been largely restricted to channel deepening with some reduction of sinuosity.

The Shungura Meander Belt (Figs. 2-4 and 2-6) is unique in many respects. Floodplain width increases a little, averaging 2 to 4 kilometers, but sinuosity, meander length and amplitude are unusually great: 2.89, 2.43, and 1.55 kilometers respectively (Table 2-1). Mean channel width is reduced to 278 meters and presumably channel depth is greater. [4] Although some convex meanders undercut older surfaces and deposits, meanders are generally free while point-bar sequences, old channel traces as well as cut-offs are common. Levees are frequently breached by diverging overflow channels along outside banks. Rising 1 to 2.5 meters above the alluvial flats, the levees slope away at gradients of 0.6 to 0.8°; locally they may be less prominent than point-bar ridges although floodplain

---

[4] No information is available on channel depth, a serious gap in our understanding of the Omo Delta. Due to the rapid day-to-day fluctuations of water level it is also impossible to obtain meaningful measurements of water level relative to levee crest. For what it is worth, the levees are 0.5-1.5m above "mean" flood level (approximately half-bankfull?) in the drowned Delta Fringe, 1-2m at the American Mission, 5-6m in the Narok and Murle Meander Belts and about 6-8m in the Shungura sector.

48

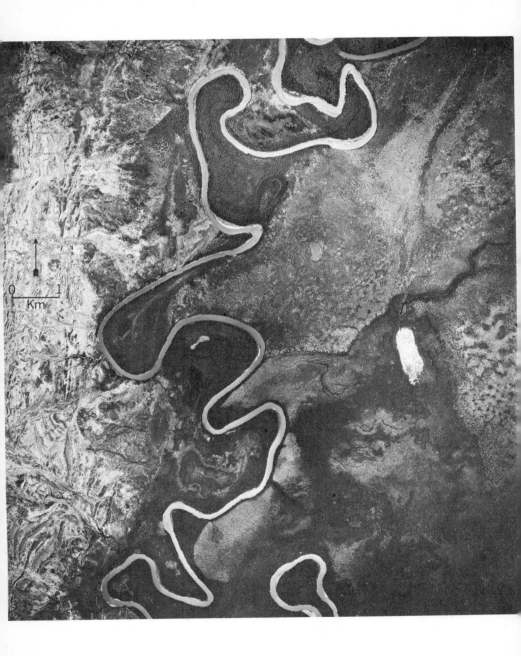

Fig. 2-4. The Shungura Meander Belt. December 1967. With permission of the Ethiopian Mapping and Geography Institute (copyright).

convexity is conspicuous. Channel incision in fairly recent times is also indicated by undercut inside and outside meander banks.

The Omo segment of the Narok Meander Belt (Figs. 2-5 and 2-7) resembles the Murle floodplain more closely. Mean channel width increases to 340 meters, but sinuosity, meander length and amplitude are drastically cut to 1.36, 1.51 and 0.90 kilometers, in that order (Table 2-1). Consequently, although the smoothly convex levee-channel axis averages 3.5 kilometers in width, with numerous clay plugs and meander scars, the Narok segment no longer meanders by strict definition. Levee relief ranges from 1 to 3 meters, with mean gradients under 0.7°. Inside and outside channel banks are undercut, and narrow silt berms complement the evidence of recent channel shortening and deepening.

The Murdizi Branch (Fig. 2-8) of the Omo is essentially fossil, although it continues to gather and drain off seepage waters along much of its course. The uppermost sector falls within the Narok Meander Belt, where the former channel has a sinuosity of 1.65, a variable meander length averaging 1.95 kilometers and a mean meander amplitude of 1.27 kilometers (Table 2-1). A channel width of only 110 to 210 meters indicates that the Murdizi channel has never been the exclusive delta arm of the Omo. Levee inclination is minimal and total channel relief today seldom exceeds 4 meters. After the initial few meander loops, the Murdizi channel rapidly loses sinuosity as wave length increases and the immediate floodplain meso-environment narrows. This in part reflects on two older, abandoned channels, the first of which is now indistinct, the later of which is still clearly marked, with attendant multiple channel traces (see Fig. 2-2). The sediment sequences that filled in the Murdizi Branch channel as it became defunct are discussed further below.

Sedimentology and Soils. The primary bed-load of the Omo River consists of a medium-grained sand (Sample No. 1090, Appendix B), discolored by abundant biotite and ferro-magnesian minerals. Initially unconsolidated and uncohesive, the horizontal, wavy or cross-bedding is moderately marked with sorting good. Exposed sand bars along inside channel bends show ripple patterns modified by wind sculpture (see section Fig. 2-9A).

Although comparable sands are the major, permanent deposit of the channel, finer sediments are laid down whenever the flood surge wanes temporarily, and particularly as the annual flood begins to recede. The two extremes of such mixed bed or suspended sediments are illustrated by the sandy loam (No. 1092) and the silty clay (No. 1050) retrieved from a backwater between a sand bar and the channel bank. However, few such deposits survive the initial flood surge of the next high water season, when they are promptly eroded and put back into saltation or suspension. The most permanent suspended sediments within the channel are the silt bars, berms or embankments accreted against inside river bends. These usually consist of brown, moderately-sorted, silty clay loams, often

50

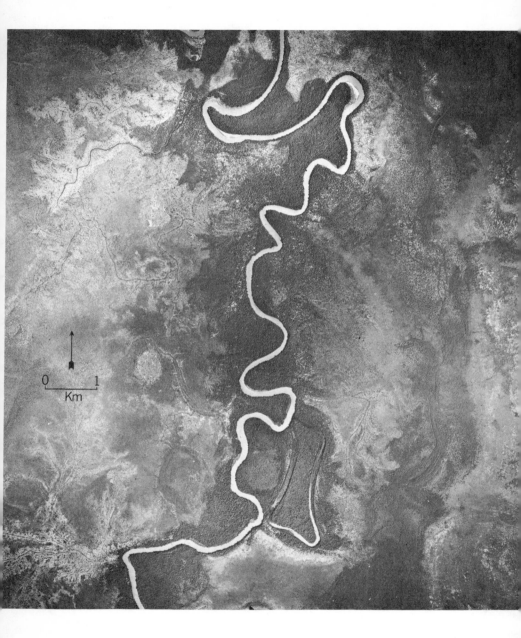

Fig. 2-5. The Narok Meander Belt with Eastern Flood Basin and part of the western Delta Flats. December 1967. With permission of the Ethiopian Mapping and Geography Institute (copyright).

well-stratified or laminated (Nos. 965, 1047-49, 1051, 1093, 1096, and 1272-74).[5] Heavy mineral content is again high, with hornblende, pyroxenes and biotite dominant, while montmorillonite and a little kaolinite constitute the clay minerals (No. 965, analyzed by F. H. Brown).

The true levees that follow the Omo channel consist in major part of subhorizontal overbank silts, in part also of former silt bars and berms. The overbank and channel silts are identical in composition, i.e. finely stratified, brown, silty clay loams (Nos. 887, 1046, 1091, 1094 and 1098-99). However, incipient limonitic mottling is not unusual with soil aeration excellent near the levee crests.

The sediments of the upper Murdizi Branch, 2 kilometers due east of Narok, are also of interest (see Fig. 2-9). The former levees, which only rise 2.5 to 3 meters above the channel floor, consist of the standard brown, silty clay loam (No. 1097, with 22.5% clay), while the two generations of silt bars are little different (No. 1096, with 21% clay). The final deposits are backwater clays, with massive, cracking properties and a silty clay texture (No. 1095, with 44% clay). Evidently the last major function of the Murdizi Branch was to serve as an overflow carrying flood silts that gradually choked off the channel. The clays were probably laid down by a combination of sporadic overbank discharge, seepage waters from gathering streams of the Eastern Flood Basin, and local runoff.

The contemporary soils of the levees and silt berms of the meander belt show moderate humification, weak horizonation and moderate depth. Color is typically brown (10 YR 4-5/3) and little different from that of the parent material. Structure is moderate, generally subangular, medium blocky, with granular aggregates present in the top 10 to 20 centimeters and coarse aggregates below 40 to 60 centimeters. Except for rooting, the organic component (probably averaging 1-2% by weight) is mainly diffuse. There are no free carbonates, pH values typically range from 6.6 to 7.0 and exchange capacity is presumably high in view of the montmorillonitic clays. The two analyses of available plant nutrients (Table 2-4) seem to suggest that the nitrogen level is variable and generally not high, while manganese is very low or deficient. Available phosphorus and potassium appear to decline rapidly with depth. There are a few fine, faint to distinct mottles below depths of 20 to 50 centimeters.

A representative profile was sampled by C. J. Carr on a silt levee in the Narok Meander Belt 6 kilometers NE of Narok (see Appendix B and Table 2-4):

0-10 cm (A1-horizon). Brown (10 YR 4/3), silty clay loam with moderate, granular to medium, angular blocky structure. Diffuse humus (2.2% organic matter) and numerous root hollows. 33% clay-size fraction, 16% sands. A relatively high pH (7.4) suggests some sodium salts may be present. (No. 1272.)

---

[5] On a fully functional floodplain these silts would be largely deposited by overbank discharge, instead of in the low-turbulence sectors of a slightly incised channel.

Fig. 2-6. The Shungura Meander Belt seen from North. Ox-bow lake, fringing levee forest and backswamp in foreground; Murle Lake Plain to left; with meander train in background. August 1967 (K.W.B.).

Fig. 2-7. Fringing Levee Forest and Silt Berm in Narok Meander Belt. The huts are on the levee crest. July 1968 (K.W.B.).

TABLE 2-4

ORGANIC MATTER AND MINERAL LEVELS OF SELECTED SOILS
(Courtesy of Emmett E. Schulte, Madison)

Sample	Organic Matter	Available				Total N
		P_2	K	Mn	Zn	
1044	0.6%	171 ppm	417 ppm	2.4* ppm	12.4 ppm	248 ppm
1045	1.2	432	567	1.1*	10.7	367
1048	1.5	125	290	---	---	---
1049	2.6	70	390	---	---	---
1050	1.8	100	470	---	---	---
1051	1.0	130	350	---	---	---
1052	1.1	185	415	---	---	---
1056	1.9	---	---	---	---	---
1057	1.9	---	---	---	---	---
1058	1.5	---	---	---	---	---
1088	0.9	168	456	1.4*	9.6	211
1089	1.9	30	895	---	---	---
1091	1.8	197	1800	2.3*	12.2	664
1094	1.0	168	366	3.9	10.0	366
1101	1.8	165	305	---	---	---
1102	0.9	190	270	---	---	---
1103	1.2	136	406	3.8	11.4	455
1106	0.9	180	740	30.0	11.4	1045
1107	1.2	71	578	20.5	10.7	347
1131	0.9	>250	465	---	---	---
1272	2.2	185	1120	---	---	---
1273	1.4	130	330	---	---	---
1274	1.5	105	235	---	---	---
1302	0.7	86	319	1.6*	10.0	380

*Indicates mineral deficiency.

10-40 cm (A2-horizon). Brown (10 YR 5/3), silty clay loam with moderate, medium-to-coarse, subangular blocky structure. Diffuse humus (1.4% organic matter). 31% clay fraction, 13% sands. pH 7.0. (No. 1273.)

40-70$^+$ cm (B-horizon). Brown (10 YR 4/3), silty clay loam with moderate, coarse, subangular blocky structure. Root impressions (1.5% organic matter). Distinct, irregular limonitic banding. 35% clay fraction, 5% sands. pH 7.0. (No. 1274.)

Clearly the delimitation of A and B horizons is a technical one that can hardly be undertaken in the field since the textural and structural differences are gradual and minute. The very limited eluviation indicated probably is of a mechanical nature. This profile is that of a classic Brown Vega soil in the terminology of Kubiena (1953: 162f.), and comparable profiles are present on well-drained silts elsewhere in the delta plain.

Evolution of the Meander Belt. The recent history of the Omo delta plain finds a substantial record in its meander belts. Innumerable meander scars and other channel

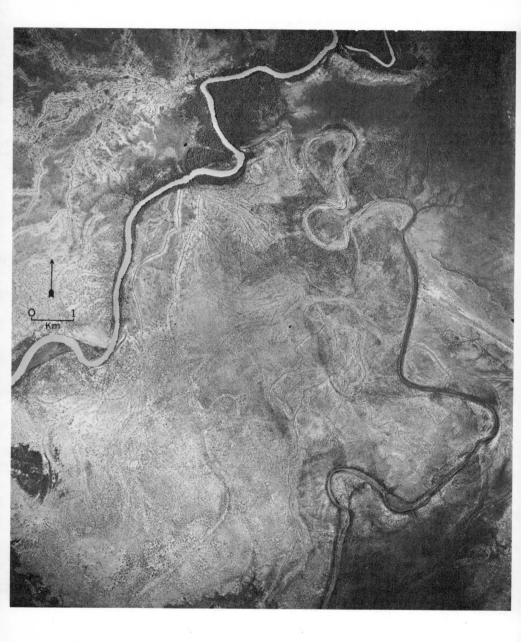

Fig. 2-8. The Murdizi Branch with the Central and part of the western Delta Flats. The Nargi Beach Ridge is conspicuous right center. December 1967. With permission of the Ethiopian Mapping and Geography Institute (copyright).

traces can be seen from the air, and from the beginning of this investigation it seemed necessary to unravel the succession of channel patterns. Thanks to the air photos, this did ultimately prove to be feasible, and Fig. 2-10 shows 4 major stages in the evolution of the meander belt.

The present configuration of the meander belt was already established in 1899 (see chapter 3), when most or all of the ox-bow lakes and other cut-offs had already been detached from the main Omo channel. Helicopter flights over the ox-bow lakes, the Lake Dipa cut-off, and several of the other more prominent meander scars, showed that these features were relatively young, and they point to a reduction in channel length, reducing the sinuosity of all three segments of the meander belt. On the basis of freshness of forms, close and recognizable links with the present channel, as well as the vegetation of cut-offs and meander scars, it is possible to reconstruct a period of greater channel sinu-osity ("stage 3") preceding the modern channel pattern ("stage 4"). Atrophy of the ox-bow lakes ("stage 3b") was a little later than deterioration of the other meanders ("stage 3a") and appears to have been contemporary with the final modifications of the Murdizi channel (Stage 3b). A fairly fresh, alternate channel of the middle Murdizi, as well as several channel scars of the Omo below Narok, must be considered as broadly contemporary with the early phases of Stage 3(a).

Stage 3 marks the maximum sinuosity of the present meander belts, with indices varying from 1.72 to 3.25 (Table 2-2). Meander wave lengths can readily be measured for the reconstructed channel trace (Fig. 2-10, Table 2-3), with a significant increase for the Narok segment. Assuming that discharge has not changed, and since meander length is directly proportional to channel width,[6] Stage 4 would indicate a general decrease in channel width with a concomitant increase in channel depth. The alternative explanation is one of reduced discharge. As discussed above, the channel morphology gives clear and ubiquitous evidence of recent channel incision, and it is improbable that changes in dis-charge would effect the Shungura and Narok Meander Belts unequally. In other words, channel width and depth did not change primarily in response to waning discharge. The best explanation is an increase in stream gradient resulting from a change in base-level, i.e. a falling lake level, although there may well have been a simultaneous decline in dis-charge.[7] Since the adjustments of meander geometry had been largely completed before 1899, the present meander configuration reflects the steady state of at least the last 70 years. Possibly the continued aggradation of silt berms within the Omo channel is the

---

[6]The relationship is $L = aW^b$, where L is wave length, W is channel width, while a and b are constants, the latter approximating 1 (Morisawa, 1968: 142).

[7]The relationship between effective or dominant discharge and wave length are dis-cussed by Leopold et al. (1964: 296f.).

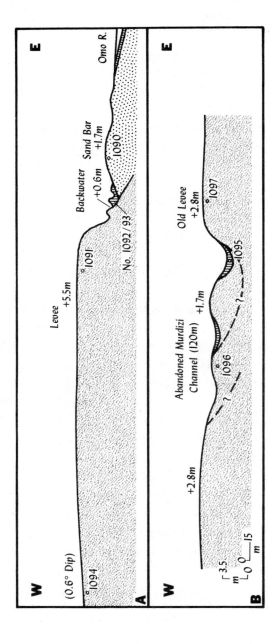

Fig. 2–9. (A) Section of Omo west Bank, 12 km NNE of Narok; (B) Section of upper Murdizi Branch, 2 km east of Narok.

first symptom of a pending readjustment of gradient to the renewed rise of lake level during the 1960's.[8]

The development of the meander belt before Stage 3 cannot be reconstructed with comparable confidence but there can be little argument about the progressive increase of sinuosity and reduction of wave length along the Shungura and Narok segments. At first the river was almost straight below the apex of the delta plain. Eventually meanders developed as sinuosity and wave amplitude increased. These two phases are captured in the abstraction of Stages 1 and 2 (Fig. 2-10). The river trace of Stage 1 is the oldest that can be reconstructed from the air photos, while Stage 2 gives a slightly more arbitrary, intermediate development between Stages 1 and 3. Although the details are not conclusive, and not all channel segments are contemporary with the channel traces so drawn, the over-all picture does possess a reasonable validity. Except for a stretch of the Shungura area, the meander geometry of Stage 2 can be approximated, as in Tables 2-2 and 2-3, while at least the sinuosity index can be estimated for Stage 1, as in Table 2-2.

The earliest evolution of the meander belts can best be interpreted in relation to a falling lake level immediately following recession from the Murle Lake Plain. At first one or more alternate channels were excavated through these old lake beds (see Figs. 2-2 and 2-10, Stage 0), probably as Lake Rudolf receded. As the lake level stabilized, the river began to readjust its course across the extensive old lake flats, gradually changing from a sinuous channel (Stage 1) to a meander belt (Stage 2) showing no longitudinal differentiation between the Shungura and Narok sectors. Conditions represented by Stage 1 seem to compare closely with those now found along the Omo downstream of Narok, or along the lower Murdizi Branch. Towards the end of Stage 2, Lake Rudolf probably began to rise again, leading to the readjustments reflected in the meander geometry of Stage 3.

More detailed time-estimates will be possible further below, after the other lines of evidence have been presented and a chronological framework established (see chapter 3). For the time being the evolution of the meander belt can be summarized in relative terms only:

(i) Dissection of the Murle Lake Plain with approximation of the modern Omo profile. Base-level falling rapidly.

(ii) Stage 1. The Omo River develops a straight to sinuous channel across the emergent lake flats. Base-level stabilizing.

(iii) Stage 2. The meander belt is created as sinuosity and wave amplitude increase. Base-level stable at first, then rising.

(iv) Stage 3a. The sinuosity of the meander belt remains stable (Narok and Murle segments) or increases (Shungura segment) as wave amplitude increases and wave length declines. Base-level high.

---

[8] This is supported by recent silt berms occasionally found embanked within outside channel bends of the Omo River upstream of Lake Lokulat.

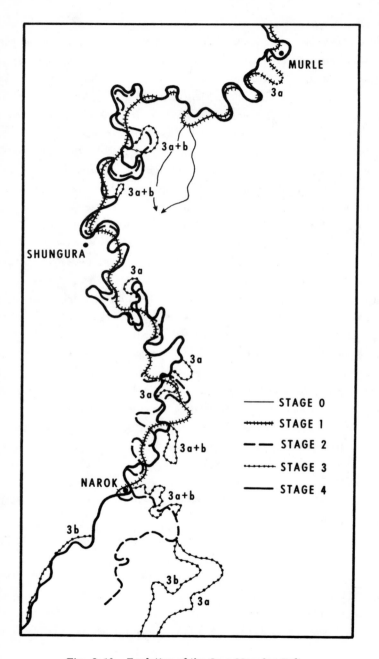

Fig. 2-10. Evolution of the Omo Meander Belts

Fig. 2-11. Buried Vertisol, 5 km NNE of Narok. July 1968 (K. W. B.)

(v) Stage 3b. Gradual reduction in both sinuosity and wave length, with channel shortening and narrowing underway. Base-level low or falling.

(vi) Stage 4. Further reduction in sinuosity with channel incision. Base-level essentially stable, although now rising.

Subsurface Deposits and Paleosols. In the southern part of the Narok Meander Belt, older clayey beds are frequently exposed along the Omo river banks. These are only preserved where multiple channel traces do not cross the present river and can be followed from about 8 kilometers upstream, where they stand 3 meters above mean flood level, to 4 kilometers downstream of Narok, where they dip below water level. A representative section is present on the west bank, 2.2 kilometers northwest of Narok (Appendix B and Table 2-4, Fig. 2-11).

(a) Over 2m exposed. Massive, brown (10 YR 5/3.5) silty clay with medium to coarse, angular blocky to prismatic structure. Diffuse humus (0.6% organic matter) and some rooting. Distinct, moderate-sized mottling common. pH values range 6.8-7.3, mV reading +150. 40.5% clay-size fraction, 0.6% sands (No. 1044).

(b) 60 cm. Massive, brown (10 YR 4.5/3) silty clay with coarse angular blocky to prismatic structure, crack networks and some slickensides. Diffuse humus (1.2% organic matter) but low nitrogen and manganese levels. Few, distinct, moderate-sized mottles. pH values range 7.7-8.1, mV readings +110 to +160. 45.5% clay fraction, 2.5% sands (No. 1045). Commonly subdivided by lenses of material as (a).

(c) 0-60 cm. Discontinuous lenses identical to (a).

(d) 2m. Well-stratified, brown (10 YR 5/3), silty clay loam with medium, subangular blocky structure. Rooting throughout, with diffuse humus in top 60 cm. pH values range 6.9-7.9, mV reading +165. 28% clay fraction, 7.5% sands (No. 1046).

The basal silty clay of this profile suggests a delta basin or prodeltaic deposit, with emergence and Vertisol development indicated by the interfingering horizons of beds (b) and (c). The top silt beds mark a fluvial regime and suggest channel silt bars. The age of the Vertisol is a little uncertain. The clayey deposits may well relate to the time of the Murle Lake Plain, in which case the Vertisol would be little older than Stage 1. Considerably less likely in terms of sedimentation rates, is the association of the massive clay strata and the Vertisol (over 3m in total thickness!) with the younger transgression implied by Stage 3a.

The Eastern Flood Basin

The Eastern Flood Basin has an area of 65 square kilometers, extending 25 kilometers from north to south and averaging 2.5 kilometers in width. A number of overflow channels breach the eastern levees of the Meander Belt and drain over very gentle inclines (0.2-2.0°) into the low flood basin via disperal streams. The lowlands, in turn, are marked by two backswamps in the northern, Shungura sector (Fig. 2-12), with an increasingly efficient network of gathering streams in the central and southern, Narok sector. Corresponding to the increasing amount of seepage water, the southern part of these flats is covered by dense woodland, contrasting with savanna and grassland to the north.

For the most part, the Flood Basin is mantled by an unknown thickness of overbank silts, with a local relief of only 2 to 4 meters, and ranging in texture from silty clay loams to silty clays, with Brown Vega profiles. The lowest areas, including the two backswamps, are poorly drained and characterized by massive, dark grayish brown, cracking clays (Nos. 1088-89) (also Fig. 2-13). The structure of these clays (60-70% in clay fractions) is angular, very coarse blocky to prismatic, with slickensides in evidence. There is a variety of macro-, meso- and micro-crack networks that penetrate to depths of over

Fig. 2-12. View northwards across the Eastern Flood Plain. The grassy stretch marks the larger of the two backswamps. August 1968 (K. W. B.).

Fig. 2-13. Cracking Vertisol, Sanderson's Gulf. July 1969 (K. W. B.).

100 centimeters and create considerable micro-topographic differentiation into small, shallow basins, i.e. gilgai phenomena as a result of the swelling-and-cracking dynamics. Prominent, moderate mottling seems to be common in the better-drained of these clays. With a moderate organic content (0.9-1.9% for Nos. 1088-89), nitrogen and manganese appear to be deficient (Table 2-4). These cracking soils are typical Vertisols or Tirs, and belong to the general category of dark tropical clays (see Dudal, 1965).

This geomorphologic meso-environment serves as a flood basin for the Meander Belt and by a strict definition also functions as part of the Omo Floodplain. However, it has served as a lagoonal mudflat of the delta as recently as 1900 (see chapter 3) and forms an integral part of the overall delta plain.

The Delta Flats

General Properties. The several Delta Flats comprise an area of almost 370 square kilometers and are notable for their subdued topography, with a local relief of 1 to 4 meters. They consist of a number of non-functional distributary complexes reflecting repeated channel bifurcation and divergence within a broad zone of former interdistributary flood basins and lagoons.

Depending on their relative age and location, the multiple distributary channels may be obscured by a veneer of younger deposits or they may be fresh and periodically utilized as overflow channels for overbank discharge from the Omo River. The more active of these channels are about 15 to 25 meters wide from bank to bank, with a depth of 3 or 4 meters. The surficial sediments of such fossilized distributaries are brown, silty clay loams comparable to other overbank silts (No. 1100). Brown Vega soils are typical.

The former mudflats and lagoons are flat and undifferentiated at ground level, but a variety of features can be recognized from the air on the basis of surface color and vegetation, differences largely due to local drainage and textural peculiarities. Much or most of the surface is veneered with silts, but this does not impede the development of the great crack networks widespread on the Delta Flats (Figs. 2-14 and 2-15). Such cracks are 1 to 1.5 meters wide and as much as 5 or more meters deep. They occur singly as well as in polygonal or rectangular arrangements, as much as 200 meters to a side. Individual cracks have vertical sides and drain by subterranean piping, resembling the ponors of karst country; enlargement proceeds by headward erosion, soil falls and piping, eventually leading to a dendritic system of tributary master-rills. Giant crack networks appear to be associated with clayey subsurface soils (Nos. 1101-03) or tracts of Vertisols. The local surface normally is undulating, with a local relief of about 1 meter and slopes of up to 1°, provided by high-centered polygons that are some 50 to 80 meters in diameter and recall giant tundra polygons. These undulations may sometimes be related to gilgai phenomena but they are more probably due to filled-in crack systems now largely obscured.

Fig. 2-14. Giant Crack with developing Tributary Network in Southern Delta Flats. August 1968 (K.W. B.).

Fig. 2-15. Giant Crack Networks in Delta Fringe emphasized by recent submergence. July 1968 (K.W. B.).

64

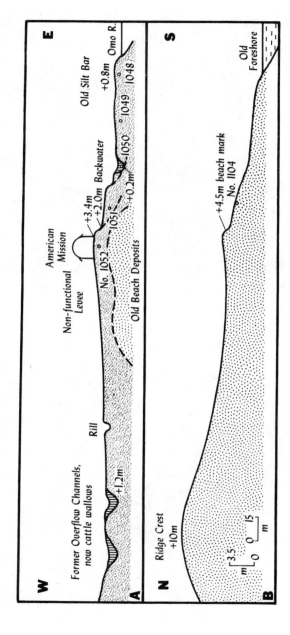

Fig. 2-16. (A) Section of the Omo River at Kaalam Mission; (B) Section of the Nargi Beach Ridge.

In addition to these crack networks of the former interdistributary basins there are rectangular and polygonal forms, often with a broadly curvilinear arrangement, that run parallel and perpendicular to former interdistributary levees and are developed in over- bank silts (Nos. 1302-03). All of these giant cracks pose a major geomorphic problem to be discussed further below.

The contemporary, fluvial meso-environments of the Delta Flats are of two kinds: the Omo River proper, and the zones of atrophied drainage lines that continue to channel seepage water, sporadic overbank discharge and local runoff (Fig. 2-17). The Omo flood- plain is relatively narrow compared to the width of the channel. The seasonally-inundated alluvial surface is largely confined to interchannel flats or silt berms that lie between the levees and high-water channels (see Fig. 2-16), many of them representing abandoned river segments. Total width of this active alluvial zone, with its channel and overbank silts (Nos. 1048-50), averages less than 0.5 kilometer (Figs. 2-18 and 2-19). The young aspect of this straight Omo channel is complemented by the absence of a well-developed fringing forest (Carr, n.d.), a fact already noted in 1933 by Arambourg (1944: 189).

Apart from the Murdizi Branch, discussed previously, the only other active drain- age system of interest is the Kaalam River (see Figs. 2-2 and 2-20). This peculiar stream begins as an ex-distributary only 25 meters in width that carries overflow water from the Omo River at the height of the flood in September. In mid-course the Kaalam functions as a gathering stream, collecting seepage and overbank discharge from two fossil distribu- tary complexes. At this point a maximum width of 150 to 175 meters is attained, with a depth of 3 to 5 meters. In its lower course the Kaalam bifurcates repeatedly into a num- ber of minor distributaries within a small basin delta, linked to the Omo channel by sev- eral gathering streams. Water from the Omo backs up into this deltaic basin during flood stage, with normal drainage at other times of the year. According to Atiko Akiru there may be discharge from one end of the Kaalam to the other during September, but this ceases by October and the whole system is dry by December. The central and lower chan- nel may also fill with local runoff (and seepage) during a good rainy season in April or May. Clearly the present discharge is inadequate to explain a river of this size, and the Kaalam must owe its origin to a time when the fossil distributary complexes were still semi- functional but the Western Delta Flats had already emerged.[9] However, in view of its straight course and lack of levees the Kaalam River seems never to have been more than a major gathering stream and incidental overflow channel.

---

[9]According to C. J. Carr (n.d.) older natives recall when the Kaalam was a major river and when the Western Delta Flats were (seasonally?) inundated.

Fig. 2-17. The Central Delta Flats with defunct, minor distributaries (foreground) and meanders of the Murdizi Branch (background). July 1968 (K. W. B.).

Fig. 2-18. Atrophied Channel Segment along the Dielerhiele Branch (Subdelta B3). July 1968 (K. W. B.).

Origin of the Giant Crack Networks. The fundamental relationship of giant crack networks to swelling-and-cracking clays can best be illustrated by a sediment section taken 4 kilometers northwest of Narok from a typical basin with an undulating floor (Appendix B and see Table 2-4):

> -60 cm. Stratified to laminated, brown (10 YR 5/3) silty clay with very coarse, angular blocky to prismatic structure. Diffuse humus (1.8% organic matter) and some rooting. Prominent and common mottling of ped faces and in subhorizontal lines. 33.5% clay-size fraction, 0.5% sands; pH 6.1-6.3 (No. 1101).

> -120 cm. Stratified, brown (10 YR 5/3) silty clay loam and clay, the former facies with few but distinct mottles, the latter with very fine salt efflorescences. Medium to coarse angular blocky structure. Diffuse humus (0.9% organic matter) and some rooting. 32.5 to 50.0% clay fraction, 0.5% sands; pH 6.4-6.7 (Nos. 1102 A, B).

> -180 cm. Stratified, brown (10 YR 4.5/3) clay with very coarse angular blocky to prismatic structure. Diffuse humus (1.2% organic matter). 48 to 54.5% clay fraction, 0.5-1.0% sands; pH 5.9-6.9 (Nos. 1103 A, B).

It can be noted that slickensides are absent, that the limited Vertisol dynamism has not destroyed the original stratification, that clay content is not excessive (see also Nos. 1302-03), and that sodium salts play a very limited role. Clearly the cracks are not due to massive subsurface salt leaching nor to gilgai phenomena.

Observation of comparable crack networks in different meso-environments of the Omo and Lomogol deltas and Sanderson's Gulf suggests that these features are associated with: (a) a considerable but not excessive component of expandable clays; (b) subterranean drainage by piping;[10] and (c) permeable materials at depth, possibly sands or loams. A sequence of development can be suggested:

(1) Seasonal cracking of a thick mantle (at least 3 or 4m) of silty clay or clay over a deep subsurface aquifer.

(2) As water drains rapidly down minor crack networks, piping begins to develop along major crack intersections.

(3) If the subsurface drainage is sufficiently rapid the pipes grow, with development of minor, subsidiary pipes below the surface and rill-cutting at ground level. Eventually funnel-like sinkholes--clay ponors--develop, producing a pitted topography.

(4) Rill-cutting, gullying and piping create linear or rectangular drainage systems tributary to the clay ponors by following the major, local cracking lines. The giant cracks so created are therefore erosional in origin, despite their affinities to the inherent dynamism of cracking clays.

(5) Giant cracks ultimately become the focus of an internal, centripetal drainage system enlarged by regressive erosion. Several such cracks may intersect and, in the most advanced stage, a dendritic badlands topography is created.

---

[10]For discussion of piping as a potent geomorphic agent see Parker (1964), also Leopold et al. (1964: 446f.).

Fig. 2-19. Flood Stage along the Erdete Branch (Subdelta B3). September 1967 (K. W. B.).

Fig. 2-20. The Kaalam River, looking south. July 1968 (K. W. B.).

Evolution of the Omo Subdeltas. The many atrophied delta complexes within the Omo delta plain document a history of shifting river channels and fluctuating lake levels. These successive subdeltas can be mapped on the criteria of distributary bifurcation, multiple major distributaries and conspicuous convexity of terrain. On these grounds a total of 10 subdeltas can be recognized (see Fig. 2-21).

Morphologically and functionally, these subdeltas can be grouped into three categories:

(A) Distributary complexes that are fully emergent and non-functional except for sporadic overflow waters and the drainage of seepage and local runoff. Four subdeltas fall into this class, all located in the Western and Central Delta Flats.

(B) Distributary complexes that either (1) have been superseded by younger subdeltas while remaining basically functional, or (2) have atrophied and become submerged. The forms of these subdeltas indicate a somewhat similar age and all are distinctly younger than group A but older than group C. Four cases fall into this class, two of which are in the Southern Delta Flats and two in the Delta Fringe.

(C) Active, primary subdeltas, including the contemporary Erdete and Dielerhiele embouchures in the now partly-submerged Delta Fringe.

Within the above classes the 10 subdeltas can be approximately ranked according to age.

For the A group, freshness of form is the only criterion by which the oldest (A1) would be considered to be the small subdelta that extends beyond the last, westward swing of the Shungura Meander Belt. The next (2A) appears to be the distributary complex issuing south of Narok, across the Central Delta Flats. The third youngest (A3) would be the well-defined subdelta northwest of Narok, while the last (A4) is the deltaic zone near the terminus of the Kaalam River. All of these Omo subdeltas are older than the beach ridges northeast of the American Mission (Fig. 2-2, and ridge W3 in Fig. 2-16). Furthermore, all appear to be related to the high lake level contemporary with Stage 3a of the Meander Belt and no older distributary complexes can be recognized in the surface morphology of the delta plain.

The subdeltas of the C group are well documented. They have formed since 1933 (see 1:500,000 folding map in Arambourg, 1944) and while the Erdete subdelta (C1) was the primary delta in 1940-41 (see 1:250,000 map of 1943), it had begun to atrophy well before 1959 (RAF aerial photography), at which time the Dielerhiele subdelta (C2) was both more active and prograded further.

The intermediate group is more difficult to sort out. Subdeltas along the upper Erdete (B3) and Dielerhiele (B4) Branches were functional in 1933 (see Arambourg, 1943), with B4 morphologically appended to B3 and consequently a little younger. The Murdizi subdeltas are older, predating any of the historical sources since 1888 (see chapter 3).

70

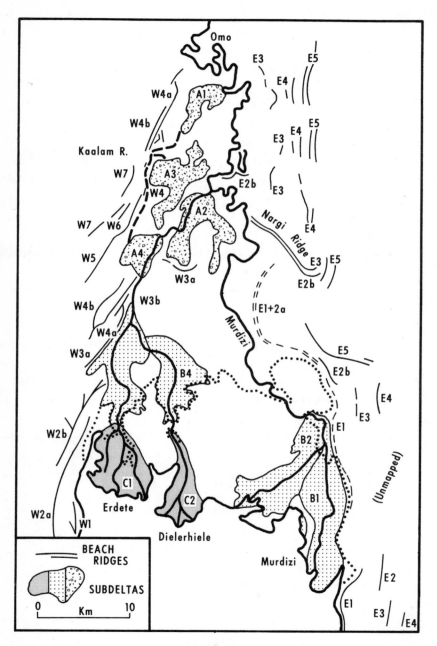

Fig. 2-21. Subdeltas and Beach Ridges of the Omo Delta Plain

Internally, the western Murdizi subdelta (B2) is higher and more distinct than the eastern counterpart (B1), which represents a swampy, low-relief subdelta on the 1959 air photos. This suggests that B1 may be older than B2.[11] Since B1 and B2 are situated rather lower than B3 and B4, a moderate rise of lake level must separate them.

Summarizing the sequence of distributary complexes:

(i) Subdelta A1.	Maximum submergence.	(Stage 3a)
(ii) Subdelta A2.	Partial emergence.	(Stage 3a)
(iii) Subdelta A3.	Submergence.	(Stage 3a)
(iv) Subdelta A4.	Partial emergence.	(Stage 3a)
(v) Subdeltas B1 and B2.	Extensive emergence.	(Stage 3b)
(vi) Subdeltas B3 and B4.	Partial submergence.	(Stage 3b?)
(vii) Subdelta C1.	Further emergence.	(Stage 4)
(viii) Subdelta C2.	Maximum emergence, then resubmergence.	(Stage 4)

The Delta Fringe

The now-submerged Delta Fringe is perhaps the most important of the deltaic environments of the Omo River: it elucidates the processes operating--past and present-- in the transitional fluvio-lacustrine environments of the Omo delta plain. It is now next to impossible to observe such processes except along the northern perimeter of the Delta Fringe. Consequently, despite field survey by helicopter and boat, the 1957-59 aerial photography is of primary importance. The subsequent discussion assumes conditions as they existed during the late 1950's, when the Delta Fringe had an area of approximately 400 square kilometers.

The extreme birdfoot profile of the contemporary shoreline (Fig. 2-22) is largely due to the Dielerhiele distributary extending 12 kilometers out into the lake--rivalled by the Erdete Branch, with a projection of over 6 kilometers, and by the remnants of the Murdizi channels. The older aerial photography also exhibits a birdfoot profile, but far less pronounced and with notable differences. Whereas the emergent projections today are largely limited to distributary levees and some shoals, the indentations of the 1950's were a matter of interdeltaic bays.

The individual distributaries of the Dielerhiele Subdelta (C2), formerly projecting 1 or 2 kilometers into the lake, were built up of successive shallow bars, with cuspate forms on the western, leeward side of each channel mouth, and tongues of highly turbid

---

[11] An alternative explanation would be to assume that Murdizi B1 reflects the final stages of flood overflow along the Murdizi Branch, at a time when the sediment load was small and restricted to silts and clays.

72

Fig. 2-22. The Erdete (left) and Dielerhiele (right) Branches (Subdeltas B3 and
B4), with general evidence of recent submergence and atrophied minor distributaries.
Note beach ridges W3a, 3b, 4a and 4b (top left). December 1967. With permission of the
Ethiopian Mapping and Geography Institute (copyright).

Fig. 2-23. The Erdete and Dielerhiele Branches (Subdeltas C1 and C2), prior to submergence. Note the turbid currents at the head of the lake. February 1959. Ministry of Defence (Air Force Department) photograph, British Crown copyright reserved.

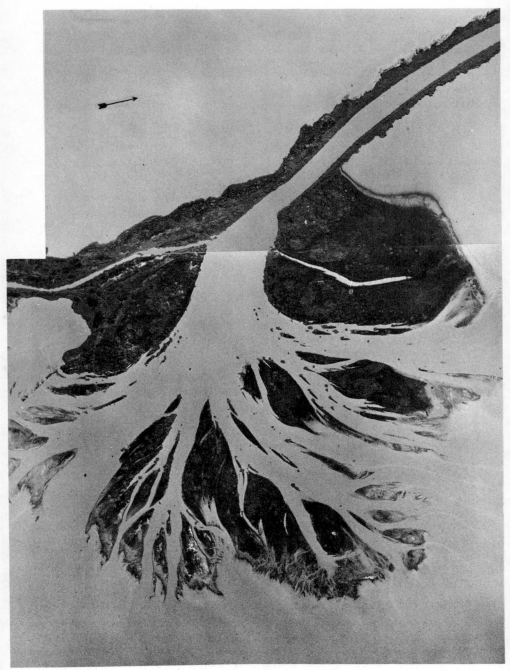

Fig. 2-24. Distributary Mouth Shoals of the Dielerhiele Branch (Subdelta C2).
June 1970. Photo courtesy of R. I. M. Campbell.

water extending 1 or 2 kilometers beyond each (Fig. 2-23). Small, poorly-defined barrier bars had begun to form in the broader, open, interdistributary bays. In general, silty sediments were and probably remain typical of subaqueous bars and shoals accumulating near the distributary mouths (Fig. 2-24) or as incipient barriers along the coast.

As a result of decreasing sediment influx, the atrophying Erdete Subdelta (C1) showed extensive cuspate remodelling by wave and longshore action. The interdistributary bays were largely closed off by coalescent distributary mouth or barrier bars and organogenic shorelines were and remain strikingly well developed (Figs. 2-25 and 2-26). So, for example, the cuspate bar that once extended westward, almost to the Todenyang shore, seems to have consisted in part of floating plants, anchored to mud shoals. [12]

More conspicuous than the interdistributary bays are the bays that separate the individual subdeltas. Good examples are provided by Todenyang Bay, by the bay between the Erdete and Dielerhiele Subdeltas (C1 and C2), and by Lake Nagum, which was still connected with Lake Rudolf in 1940-41. Organogenic coastal perimeters were and remain typical, with a "floating" margin of sediment-binding, aquatic vegetation followed by stands of cattails (Typha), sedges (Cyperus), tall reeds (Phragmites) and other grasses further inshore (Carr, n.d.; also Beadle, 1932b) (Figs. 2-27 and 2-28). This organogenic shoreline reflects minimal gradients, the quasi-absence of wave activity, as well as the seasonal fluctuations of lake level. The lake floods back into such interdeltaic bays and into the interdistributary basins while the water level rises. [13] As a result, subaqueous and subaerial environments are poorly defined by comparison with deltas that develop on lakes regulated by an outlet threshold.

The interdistributary basins are occupied by lagoonal mudflats and marsh. Open water, partly or entirely camouflaged by vegetation, is found in the lower basins, often connected with the interdistributary or interdeltaic bays by small channels. The seasonally inundated marsh belt, at slightly higher elevations, is covered by a thin sheet of water for 2 to 5 months each year as the lake goes through its annual cycle with a vertical range of 90-100 centimeters, and a year-to-year variation of perhaps twice that amplitude.

---

[12] Similar islands of "floating" vegetation formerly existed in Lake Nagum. Neumann (1898: 339) describes how a storm with northerly winds detached these mats of floating vegetation " . . . the lake became dotted for miles with floating islands of various sizes, some of them with tall grass or rushes growing on them. These are evidently masses of water-weeds, detached by the strong northerly breeze from great beds of floating vegetation formed about the mouth of the river . . . on the return of the prevailing southerly wind, they all get backed up again at the northern extremity and leave the water open once more."

[13] Höhnel (1894: 202) noted a current in excess of 1 km/hr as waters backed up into a similar bay.

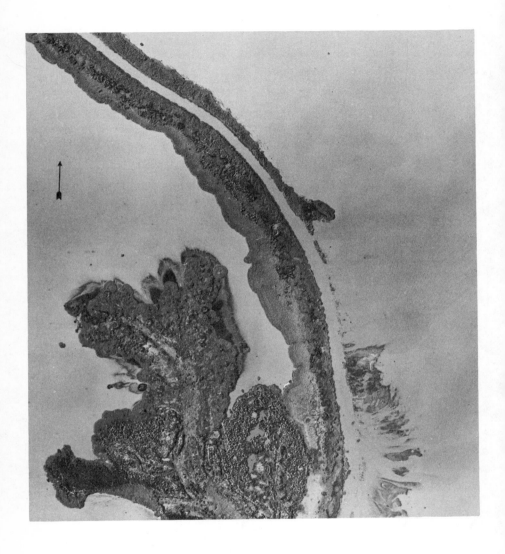

Fig. 2-25. Organogenic Deposits of atrophied Distributary Mouth, Erdete Branch (Subdelta C1). Note the submerged and breached levees at lower right, with incipient delta fan. June 1970. Photo courtesy of R. I. M. Campbell.

Fig. 2-26. Levee Morphology and Vegetation Patterns of Erdete Branch. June 1970. Photo courtesy of R. I. M. Campbell.

78

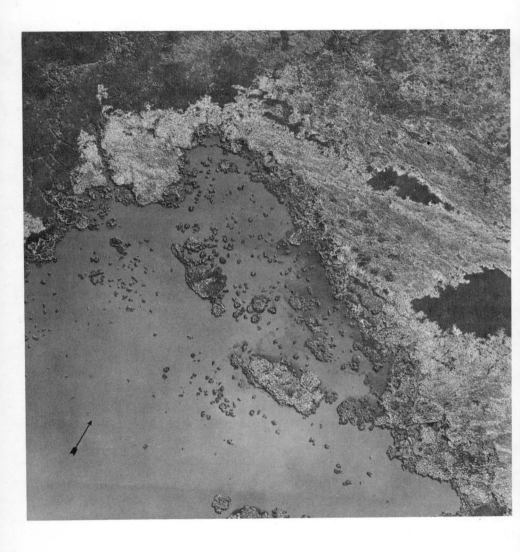

Fig. 2-27. Organogenic Shorelines east of Dielerhiele Branch. June 1970. Photo
courtesy of R. I. M. Campbell.

Sediments are mixed organic and mineral, as vegetation colonizes these flats, trapping and binding suspended sediment. The resulting deposits normally consist of a finely bedded to massive, brown (10 YR 5/3) clay, with very coarse angular blocky to prismatic structure, approximately 1% organic matter, and with neutral or slightly acid reactions (pH 6.1-6.3, compared with 6.5-7.4 for other modern fluvial deposits) (Nos. 1106-07). Limonitic mottling and diffuse or banded staining may be present, and bands of ferric concretions or more continuous limonitic bands are, theoretically, possible among these interdistributary clays at depth; they have not been observed in sections, however, and probably require quite long periods of suitable conditions in order to develop. Sodium salts, with a little gypsum,[14] are precipitated in ponds or stagnant waters during periods of desiccation and, it would seem, particularly during times of receding lake level. Such salty waters can be more widely disseminated by wind-driven lagoonal waters.[15]

The strictly fluvial sub-environment of the Delta Fringe is that of the distributaries and their natural levees (Figs. 2-29 and 2-30), which now rise 0.5 to 1.5 meters above water. Bank overflow and occasional levee breaching develop conspicuous, convex berms and silt splays adjacent to the major channels. Repeated channel deterioration and channel shifts subsequently increase the surface extent of strictly fluvial deposits. Overbank silts of the levees consist of stratified, pale brown to dark grayish brown (10 YR 4-6/2.5-3), moderately sorted, silty clay loam or silty clay (Nos. 1056-58). Fine but distinct reddish yellow mottles are common and indicate oxidation, usually along former root zones; horizontal bands of ferric staining may be present at depth but were not observed. Bedding is horizontal although turbulent, and undulating lamination can be expected in silt splays or channel proximity. Typical channel beds were not sampled but marginal samples suggest that the medium sand component (60-200 microns) is prominent. The levee vegetation today grades from tall aquatic grasses (such as Phragmites australis) with sedges and scattered brees in the Delta Fringe through numerous gradations of thickets and woodland to a continuous fringing woodland in the meander belts (Carr, n.d.).

---

[14] In 1931 Beadle (1932a) found that the alkalinity of Lake Rudolf varied from 0.0194 to 0.0216 N in deep, open water. It increased to 0.0230 N in an enclosed situation such as Ferguson's Gulf, rising to 0.113 N in small, isolated pools, where pH values were well over 10. The level of ions and anions in open lake water was measured near Central Island (in p.p.m.): Na 770, K 23, Ca 5, Mg 4, Fe and Al 3, CO_3 652, Cl 429 and SO_4 56. More recently, Walsh and Dodson (1969: 37) have published partial data from 7 samples of lake water. CO_3 ranges from 506 to 1320, Cl from 193 to 520, SO_4 from 15 to 50, and pH from 8.5 to 10.6. By contrast the one sample of Omo water yielded a pH of 7.6, showed no carbonates, with bicarbonates 156 p.p.m. and chlorides 28 p.p.m.

[15] Limited quantities of hygrophytic salts are not uncommon in many clayey beds of both the Kibish Formation (Butzer, 1970) and the Omo Beds (De Heinzelin et al., 1971).

Fig. 2-28. Vegetation Mosaics in Delta Fringe. July 1968 (K.W.B.)

Fig. 2-29. The Dielerhiele Branch (Subdelta C2), looking south. July 1968 (K.W.B.)

Fig. 2-30. Distributary Levee of Dielerhiele Branch (Subdelta C2), with crocodiles. July 1968 (K. W. B.).

Fig. 2-31. Geometric Patterns in Pond Vegetation of Delta Fringe. July 1968 (K. W. B.).

Fig. 2-32. The lower Murdizi Branch with Lake Fadja (at right), littoral deposits on edge of alluvial fan (top right), and widespread atrophied, minor tributaries and organogenic shorelines. December 1967. With permission of the Ethiopian Mapping and Geography Institute (copyright).

Cracking patterns appear to have been as common in the Delta Fringe as they now are on the Delta Flats. Of particular interest are the geometric patterns (see Fig. 2-31) conspicuous amid the aquatic vegetation (Nymphaea, Pistia, etc., Carr, n.d.) that covers the mosaic of interdistributary ponds. The only explanation that can be offered for these patterns is that the seasonal rise of water disrupts the cover of aquatic plants as the water surface expands a little.

The recent history of the Delta Fringe would be incomplete without mention of the unmistakable evidence for recent subsidence in the eastern, Murdizi sector. Here a part of the Murdizi levees and channel are downwarped adjacent to Lake Fadja (Figs. 2-32 and 2-33) and similar, differential subsidence is evident in the central parts of Murdizi Sub-deltas. These deformations can best be attributed to compaction of unconsolidated sediments.

The Prodeltaic Zone

Turbid, yellow-brown waters are evident at the northern end of Lake Rudolf at all seasons, indicating active fluvio-lacustrine sedimentation. Persistent wave activity or a strong swell assure deep mixing of the lake waters so that oxygen is abundant at all levels and temperature gradients beneath 5 meters depth are approximately isothermal.[16] Because sedimentation of suspended matter is not complicated by vertical temperature gradients, and since there is no evidence for a reducing environment in the lower layers of the lake, it is reasonable that the bottom sediments at the head of the lake should consist of broad expanses of undifferentiated clays.[17] Massive, lacustrine muds of presumed prodeltaic facies that were deposited in the modern Delta Flats during recent centuries consist of brown (10 YR) clays, such as Nos. 1044-45 or 1102-03 (Appendix B), with little evidence of either oxidation or reduction. Until bottom sediments from the northern third of Lake Rudolf[18] can be analyzed, it seems that few systematic differences can be demonstrated between "lacustrine" or "prodeltaic" clays on the one hand, and interdistributary clays on the other.

---

[16] Temperatures at depths of 5m or more appear to remain fairly constant between 26 and 28.5° C (79-83° F), with diurnal variations limited to the surface layer (Beadle, 1932a).

[17] A "uniform soft mud" according to Worthington and Ricardo (1935).

[18] A University of Miami group explored a good part of the lake floor in 1958-59 with a Raytheon fathometer. Bottom profiles from the northern end of the lake suggest one large delta from the present mouth of the Omo to the latitude of North Island (O. T. Owre, pers. comm.). The maximum known depth of Lake Rudolf is 73m.

84

Fig. 2-33. Partly drowned Murdizi Branch, with extensive burning in evidence. July 1968 (K. W. B.).

Beach Ridge Plains

The Contemporary Littorals. The littoral sub-environments of Lake Rudolf include (a) the Delta Fringe shorelines, discussed above, (b) the leeward, low wave-energy eastern coast, and (c) the windward, high wave-energy western shores.

The low wave-energy sector can be subdivided into two parts. The Murdizi subdeltas and Lake Fadja have organogenic shorelines, in part formed by belts of zoned aquatic emergents that extend 100 meters and more onto gently inclined, submerged deltaic surfaces or alluvial fans (Figs. 2-34 and 2-35). Spike rush (*Eleocharis* sp.) is found farthest out, followed by communities of sedges with *Cyperus laevigatus* and *C. articulatus* (Carr, n.d.). South of the Murdizi subdeltas, mineral shorelines are common, particularly where gradients are a little steeper and where the shoreline has not shifted much during the 1960's. A nip of 30 centimeters or so is cut into sandy beds of eolian origin (Fig. 2-36), with mixed organic muds and sands in the shallow foreshore. Above the watermark, low ridges (E1, Fig. 2-37) of well-sorted, coarse sands (No. 944) extend for several hundreds of meters inland, with very gentle slopes and few coherent patterns. The sands appear to be primarily of eolian facies, but wave reworking is apparent at the shore and true fluvial beds are found both at depth and further inland. Quartz is dominant but ferromagnesian minerals and feldspars are also present.

The high wave-energy coasts are more complex. Near Ferguson's Gulf and the Turkwell Delta low beach ridges are widespread amid a lag of reworked gravel, with a cordon of coastal dunes that attain a relief of 25 to 30 meters and more. The last include merging W-dunes, linear dunes, and minor "tied" dunes.

Further north the coastal dunes are replaced by an active beach ridge line some 10 to 25 meters wide (see Fig. 2-38), curving in broad arcs subparallel to the shore and with a relief seldom exceeding a meter or so. The lee slope rises abruptly from a smooth sandy or lag-strewn sruface, separating a chain of lagoons and ponds from the open lake. During the low-water season these ponds are often evaporated and reduced to salt pans, while others are infested with blue-green algae or diatom blooms; others still are charged with ferric solutions of uncertain origin. Inland of the post-ridge swales, the surface rises gently, and the next ridge may be 250 to 500 meters away and at relative elevations of +15 meters and more; older beach ridges of this kind are vegetated and suggest that the contemporary shore marks the highest lake stand in at least several decades. The functional beach ridge itself is normally built of moderately to well-sorted coarse sands or gravelly sands (No. 1122), including a component of shell debris, feldspars, heavy minerals and basalt sand, with cobble gravel intercalations near stream mouths. The foreshore is demarcated by a major nip but further irregularized by additional constructional features--low benches and nips, each with a relief of 20 to 50 centimeters (Fig. 2-39). Unlike

Fig. 2-34. Organogenic Shoreline along partly submerged Alluvial Fan, east of Murdizi Branch (Subdelta B1). July 1968 (K. W. B.).

Fig. 2-35. Zoned Aquatic Emergents of Low Wave-Energy Littoral, east of Murdizi Branch (Subdelta B1). July 1968 (K. W. B.).

Fig. 2-36. Low Wave-Energy Shoreline near Ileret. August 1967 (K. W. B.).

Fig. 2-37. Low Beach Ridges and old Beach Foredunes southeast of Murdizi Sub-delta B1. August 1967 (K. W. B.).

the central ridges, these micro-benches may take cuspate forms (Fig. 2-40); they are best developed on concave segments of the shore, and are transitory features related to seasonal fluctuations in lake level and, more specifically, to periods of unusually strong wave action. So, for example, in July of 1969 there were seasonal, constructional forms with benches at about 30 and 60 centimeters below a major nip recording the highest lake stand of 1968 (Fig. 2-39).

Near Todenyang, the supply of sand is greater, and the coastal ridge (W1, Fig. 2-42) assumes greater prominence, with a relief of 5 to 10 meters and mixed eolian-littoral facies (No. 1006). There are multiple ridges and intraridge swales with frequent blow-outs. Locally, vegetated hairpin dunes, some very low, silt barchans (Fig. 2-42), as well as marshland may be found in the elongated depression behind the coastal ridge complex. A second, high ridge is found 1 to 3 kilometers inland (W2, Fig. 2-42). Here vegetated beach foredunes, with a local relief of 5 to 6 meters and slopes of 2 to 5°, rest on older, lacustrine sediments at 3 meters above present lake level.

The Fossil Beach Ridges. The western margins of the delta plain are followed by a set of discontinuous beach ridges, running subparallel to each other and trending from south-southwest to north-northeast (see Figs. 2-2, 2-21 and 2-41). The maximum inclination of these ridges varies according to their freshness and degree of dissection. The youngest are almost featureless and have few slopes exceeding 1°. Those of intermediate age are more irregular, with steeper generalized slopes in the 2 to 5° range, and increasing dissection or erosion. The oldest are well dissected and eroded to a low-relief silhouette. The basic texture is one of a medium- to coarse-grained sand with fine shell debris, although many surface samples (~40cm) show the effects of humification and weathering, with higher silt contents (Nos. 1000, 1002, 1006).

A succession of such ridges has been identified and mapped. They have been labelled from W1 to W7, with identical numbers used for ridges that can be traced on the air photos from one occurrence to the next or whenever the implied lake level was measured to be identical. Relative elevations of the majority of these ridges were obtained and rechecked by altimeter, using the helicopter. The ridges, their forms, and the approximate lake levels they indicate can be listed as follows:

W1	+9 meters	(Complex, with dunal remodelling)
W2a	+3 meters	(Complex, with dunal remodelling)
W2b	+3.5 meters	(Limited relief)
W3a	+5 meters	(Limited relief)
W3b	+8 to 10 meters	(Limited relief)
W4a	+15 meters	(Moderate relief)
W4b	+20 meters	(Moderate relief)

Fig. 2-38. Bay Mouth Bar of drowned Rudolf Tributary near Lokitaung. August 1968 (K.W.B.).

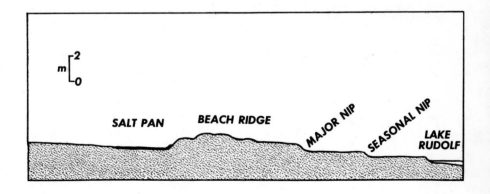

Fig. 2-39. Idealized Profile of High Wave-Energy Coast west of Lake Rudolf. Not to scale.

Fig. 2-40. High Wave-Energy Shoreline near Lokitaung, with temporary constructional benches and beach cusps. July 1969 (K. W. B.).

Fig. 2-41. The Nargi Beach Ridge, looking east. August 1968 (K. W. B.). (See
also Fig. 2-16B.)

W5	+23 meters	(Dissected, with moderate relief)
W6	+31 meters	(Dissected, with limited relief)
W7	+36 meters	(Dissected, with limited relief)

In terms of their stratigraphy, the fossil beach ridges of the eastern delta margins are less adequately understood, because of their low relief, greater areal expanse and complexity, as well as the limited vertical control established during the field work. As a result, the higher sets of ridges have necessarily been grouped. Altogether, the larger intermittent streams of the eastern delta periphery have eroded these beach ridges far more extensively. The sequence is as follows:

E1	+3 meters	(Limited relief)
E2a	+5 meters	(Limited relief)
E2b	+10 meters	(Limited relief)
E3	+15 meters	(Dissected, with moderate relief)
E4	+20 to 25 meters	(Dissected, with limited relief)
E5	+30 to 35 meters	(Dissected, with limited relief)

The development of the eastern beach ridges is highly variable according to location and sediment source. At the one extreme is the prominent Nargi Beach Ridge (E2b/3, Figs. 2-16, 2-41), with a local relief in excess of 10 meters and a generalized slope of 2-5°. This ridge consists of very coarse sand (No. 1104), in part rich in fine gravel, and owes most of its sediment and some of its prominence to a now eroded alluvial fan from the eastern drainage lines. On the other extreme is the levee backslope, east of Narok (E2b, Fig. 2-21), which--in a limited way--functioned as a barrier ridge, leading to an accentuation of relief, with a generalized slope of 2° but no conspicuous shift in sediment grade (Nos. 1098-99) from that of normal overbank silts. More intermediate but far more extensive are the low-relief and mixed littoral deposits (No. 1105) not mapped as true beach ridges on Fig. 2-2. These include the fringe of littoral features just east of the Murdizi Branch; they are all found on and intergrade with broad, sweeping alluvial surfaces. Unquestionably most common are the multiple, ridge undulations characteristic of the prolonged but fluctuating high lake level marked by the E4 and E5 complex (Fig. 2-21). These loamy sediments have gentle forms, seldom exceeding a 1° slope in profile, and grade into the dissected piedmont alluvial plain of which they once were a part. These alluvia form a widespread 4- to 5-meter terrace at the margins of the Eastern Beach Ridge Plain; they are discussed further in connection with the Murle Lake Beds.

In terms of relative age, shorelines defined by the western and eastern ridges can be broadly correlated on the basis of elevation. Admittedly, many of the beach ridges have been remodelled by repeated fluctuations and standstills of lake level. However, as a group, the dominant shoreline elevations, the relief, and the degree of dissection form a set of criteria that can be employed to discriminate stages in the fluctuations of Lake

Fig. 2-42. High Wave-Energy Beach Ridge, 5 km S of Ft. Todenyang, with barchan field in post-dunal swale. June 1970. Photo courtesy of R. I. M. Campbell.

Rudolf. The following sequence of high shorelines can be identified and related to certain of the older subdeltas and meander belt stages:

(i) <u>30 to 35-meter Shorelines</u>. A long period of high, fluctuating lake level with development of beach-ridge sets W6, W7 and E5, as well as of the dissected, 4 to 5-meter eastern piedmont alluvial plain. Directly linked with Murle Lake Plain and predating modern deltaic plain.

(ii) <u>20 to 25-meter Shorelines</u>. A complex of briefer high levels, probably marking halts in the regression from phase (i), with development of beach-ridge sets W5 and at least part of E4.

(iii) <u>15 to 20-meter Shorelines</u>. Two, relatively short transgressions, leading to the development of beach-ridge sets W4b, W4a, E3 and, possibly, a part of E4. The younger, 15-meter transgression would have completely submerged the now-functional delta plain. These shorelines would correlate well with the sequence recorded by Subdeltas A1, A2 and A3.

(iv) <u>5 to 10-meter Shorelines</u>. Two standstills in a regression from the 15-meter phase, with development of ridge sets W1, W3b, W3a, E2b and E2a, as well as remodelling of part of subdelta A2 and progradation of Subdelta A4. Predate the "B" group of subdeltas.

(v) <u>3-meter Shoreline</u>. A relatively minor but protracted transgression of Lake Rudolf, possibly younger than Subdeltas B1 and B2 but contemporary with B3.

The Murle Lake Plain

The non-functional deposits of the Murle Lake Plain (Fig. 2-2) are the oldest visible within the confines of the delta plain. Unfortunately, the implications of this geomorphic entity were only recognized in 1969, at which time there was no opportunity to undertake the necessary morphological work and sediment sampling. Consequently, the present description is limited to a summary delineation of the more salient features, together with a tentative interpretation.

The greater part of the Murle Lake Plain forms a flat and only slightly undulating surface at 3 to 8 meters above the Shungura and Murle Meander Belts (Fig. 2-43). For the main part, this low upland plain is at 25 to 30 meters above the present level of Lake Rudolf and it appears to merge with littoral deposits related to the E4 shorelines (+20 to 25m). Texture appears to be intermediate and loamy, judging by the dominance of grassland with widely dispersed trees--a vegetation pattern characteristic for the beach ridges elsewhere in the Lower Omo Basin (Carr, n.d.). Of some interest are the broad, shallow pock marks with a relief of perhaps a meter and that measure a few hundred meters in diameter. Such features are rare or poorly developed on the active delta plain but are

Fig. 2-43. Dissected Murle Lake Plain with former Omo Channel, looking south-west. July 1969 (K. W. B.).

Fig. 2-44. Kerre Village on Terrace Spur graded to Murle Lake Plain. West of Omo River, looking north. July 1969 (K. W. B.).

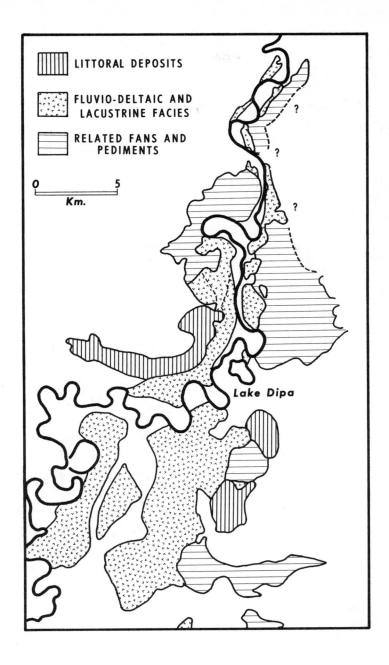

Fig. 2-45. The Depositional Record of the Murle Lake Stage from Shungura to White Sands.

common on fluvio-deltaic surfaces of the Kibish Formation. They may be a result of differential compaction.

At its margins the Murle Lake Plain rises gently, with slopes of less than 1°, to a series of undulating beach ridges (set E5), at 30 to 35 meters above the modern lake. These ridges fringe the base or developed within erosional embayments of higher ridges and piedmont alluvial surfaces that pertain to the Kibish Formation (Member IVb). The older beds and surfaces consist of coarse sands and sandy loams with gravel inclusions, and generally rise 10 meters and more above the Murle Lake Plain. A little further south, the mixed littoral deposits of the Murle transgression also grade laterally into piedmont alluvia that now form 4- to 5-meter terraces above functional, braided channels.[19] A Noncalcic Burozem examined in this alluvium, 16 kilometers due east of Shungura, exhibits a profile common to other exposures of contemporaneous piedmont deposits (see Appendix B):

0-60 cm. A1-horizon. Stratified, brown (7.5 YR 5/4) loam with strong, very coarse, angular blocky structure. With abundant macroscopic humus in top 10 cm, intensive rooting in top 20-30 cm, and diffuse humus throughout. Non-calcareous and slightly alkaline; 23% clay fraction (No. 945A).

60->340 cm. C-horizon. Stratified, pale brown (10 YR 5.5/3) loam with moderate, very coarse, subangular blocky structure. The fine gravel lenses consist of subrounded, macro- to mesocrystalline quartz, pegmatite and gneiss. Traces of salt efflorescences on peds. Non-calcareous and neutral; 20% clay fraction (No. 945B).

This soil has been truncated on a 2-meter erosional bench formed along the channel margins, and disappears where the dissected alluvium is reworked into broad, shallow fans that sweep over the edge of the Murle Lake Plain.

Upstream of Lake Dipa the related deposits form a discontinuous alluvial terrace that follows the Omo floodplain upstream to White Sands (see Figs. 2-44 and 2-45). The deposits rise 3 to 5 meters above the functional alluvium, but the relative longitudinal gradient was not established. A great variety of facies is evident, ranging from brown clayey beds and white marly(?) strata to sandier sediments away from the present river (Fig. 2-46). Presumably these are fluvio-lacustrine in origin.

The Murle Lake Plain reflects a 30- to 35-meter transgression of Lake Rudolf, with final sediment accretion apparently contemporary with the 25-meter shoreline. Except near White Sands, where terraced fills rest on Kibish units, the associated deposits everywhere extend to beneath the present stream channels. Consequently the fluvio-lacustrine facies must be at least 8 meters thick, the lateral piedmont alluvia at least 5 meters. This, together with the multiplicity of beach ridges, suggests a protracted period of time, probably longer than the span represented by the total of younger deposits and erosional features on the delta plain. Two, broad but shallow channels were cut

---

[19] The channel beds consist of coarse-sandy loams with lenses of fine-to-medium grade gravel, anastomosing between broad shoals and bars with a relief of 50 cm.

Fig. 2-46. Exposure of Murle Lake Plain Beds (see Fig. 2-39). July 1969 (K. W. B.).

Fig. 2-47. Sanderson's Gulf, looking south to Mt. Laburr across mudlfats. July 1969 (K. W. B.).

across the old lake flats during final emergence, probably at the time of the older, 20-meter shoreline. The meander belts developed subsequently, as has already been discussed above.

It appears that the Murle Lake Plain occupies an intermediate position between the youngest units of the Kibish Formation and the recent delta plain. It marks a significant and extended transgression to +35 meters that is somewhat younger than the fall of Lake Rudolf from the 70-meter shoreline of ca. 1650 B.C. Presumably a long period of relatively low lake level intervened. It will be imperative to obtain radiocarbon dates for the Murle Lake Plain. Furthermore, the associated beds deserve formational status, pending the selection and study of a suitable type section.

Sanderson's Gulf

The monotonous expanse of Sanderson's Gulf (Fig. 2-47) can be described as a 750-square kilometer sweep of alkaline mudflats and associated shore deposits. Longitudinally, this surface is 68 kilometers long and average width is almost 11 kilometers. Grassy vegetation predominates, with much bare ground and marginal thickets of Acacia in some area. In detail, the "Gulf" is surprisingly complex, despite the lack of relief and surface differentiation. Perhaps the only unifying theme is that the "Gulf" is a tectonic depression, somehow downwarped and downfaulted between the Omo Beds to the northeast and the Laburr Range to the southwest. The "Gulf" merges with the Kibish Delta to the north, the Lomogol and Meiyen deltas to the west, the Omo distributaries to the east, Lake Rudolf to the southeast, and local alluvial plains or pediments almost everywhere else. Consequently there are mixed fluvio-lacustrine beds, deltaic formations, as well as beach ridges and littoral deposits--in part reworked by eolian activity. Owing their origin to a medley of sources and processes, of different ages, these lateral facies lie athwart the periphery of the central mudflats. Altogether, it appears that Sanderson's Gulf rivals the Omo Delta Plain in complexity.

Study of the "Gulf" was limited to mapping of the surficial deposits to the base of the 1:100,000 maps, distinguishing 4 basic categories: mudflats, littoral-lacustrine beds, beach ridges, and several subtypes of peripheral alluvia. This was done on the basis of the 1959 and, where available, more recent aerial photography, with a series of helicopter overflights and ground checks in 1968 and a Land-Rover traverse in 1969. Only a few of the mudflat sediments were sampled[20] since nothing more than a general reconnaissance

---

[20] The samples listed in Appendix B include two that repeatedly flocculated during hydrometer testing and for which precise silt and clay fractions cannot be specified (Nos. 1592-93). The calcium carbonate for Nos. 1595 and 1597 was determined by the Chittick (CO_2 release) method, while that for Nos. 1592-93 was obtained from weight loss after HCl application; the latter method removed substantial amounts of sodium salts as well.

was warranted with the limited time available.

Beach ridges are poorly developed and restricted to the western margins of the "Gulf," between the Lomogol and Meiyen rivers. Undulating, low fields of littoral-lacustrine deposits are widespread along the western, southern and northeastern edge and similar deposits occur as "islands" within the mudflats in the northern half of the "Gulf." Some littoral beds in the center of the "Gulf" have been superficially remodelled to very shallow dunes of "W"-type, consisting of medium-grade sands and small clayey aggregates (Fig. 2-48). No altimetric or stratigraphic differentiation of shoreline features was attempted, although morphological resemblances suggest close parallels with the alternating submergence and emergence of the Omo Delta Plain.

Northwards, the "Gulf" flats grade almost imperceptibly into the dark cracking clays of the Kibish Delta, a zone of multiple distributaries emanating from repeated belts of bifurcation and stream divergence. Although at a smaller scale than that of the Omo, the Kibish River clearly records successive stages of recent evolution in its surficial deposits. These consist primarily of dark grayish brown, cracking clays (No. 1131). The farthest distributary arms extend deeply into the "Gulf," until they deteriorate as a series of hollows and pools, followed by fringing woodland. A fossil river channel can also be recognized somewhat further south (Fig. 2-2), indicating that the Kibish River must at one time have flowed directly into an embayment of Lake Rudolf. The Meiyen and Lomogol rivers also issue periodically into the "Gulf" from the west, via deltas of brown (10 YR) clayey sediment that dip in concave profiles at appreciably less than $1°$. The anastomosing and diverging rills, runnels, and distributaries have a local relief of 20 centimeters to 4 meters, and ultimately deteriorate into strings of shallow depressions (Fig. 2-49) that hold water long after the rains.

The lowest parts of the mudflats, most liable to flooding, consist of cracking, light brownish gray (10 YR 6/2.5) clays (Nos. 1595, 1597) (Fig. 2-13) such as those of the central and northwestern "Gulf." Unique and rich in ferric oxides are the brown (7.5 YR 4/2) clays (No. 1593) found adjacent to the Laburr drainage; these clays also have abundant montmorillonite and soda, leading to an unusual cracking dynamism based on cubic aggregates that form an expansive topsoil when dry. Gradients of silt, clay, and solubles--reflecting on proximity of Omo influx, water depth and alkalinity--seem to exist, but are not clear on present evidence. Approximately 90 square kilometers were inundated at the time of the aerial photography of December, 1967, and comparable tracts appear to be flooded each autumn. Shells of the aquatic mollusc, _Cleopatra bulimoides_, are scattered across the central and southern parts of the mudflats, suggesting that wider areas were inundated for a minimum of 5 months (see Tothill, 1946) in the relatively recent past. In the zone of contemporary, seasonal submergence _Cleopatra_ is associated with shells of

Fig. 2-48. Giant Cracking Patterns on Mudflats, Sanderson's Gulf. Note animal tracks. July 1968 (K. W. B.).

Fig. 2-49. Distributary Channel of Lomogol Delta terminating in Sanderson's Gulf. July 1969 (K. W. B.).

Pila (Ampularia),[21] an amphibious snail characteristic of temporary swamps (Tothill, 1946).

The northernmost third of the "Gulf" is at slightly higher elevations and shows a little more irregularity and relief. Any seasonal flooding is now restricted in occurrence and a result of local runoff. Texture is coarser, and clay loams (such as No. 1592) are probably symptomatic of reworked littoral sands or alluvial transport or both.

The beach ridges (W2a, W2b) that presently close off the "Gulf" from Lake Rudolf appear to be fairly young; they suggest barrier ridges that developed as Lake Rudolf receded from Sanderson's Gulf on one or more occasions. At such times the sound was changed to a lagoon and finally a seasonal playa, deriving its waters from local runoff and Omo discharge. Whether or not there have been significant changes of depositional environments remains to be determined from subsurface coring.

Contemporary Depositional Media as Taphocoenoses

It has already been emphasized that study of the contemporary delta is of primary importance to any serious interpretation of the Plio-Pleistocene sediment sequences in the Lower Omo Basin. Of further relevance are depositional environments as media for the potential burial and preservation of animal remains. Consequently, in concluding this chapter, a few comments can be directed to the theme of fossil assemblages and taphocoenoses.

The uplands of the Lower Omo Basin are not suitable for the burial or preservation of bone. The mountain and hill country is subject both to severe erosion and intensive weathering, and lavas and pyroclastics are not accumulating in the study area at the moment. Neither are the meso-environments of the upland plains favorable for fossilization. The pediment fringes are zones of erosion with thin and subcontinuous alluvial veneers that consist primarily of well-aerated, coarse sands. Significant fluvial activity on the piedmont alluvial plains is sporadic: bone is "weathered" and reduced to a dehydrated, brittle state while lying on the surface--for years prior to possible burial in sandy alluvia with good aeration and a minimum of mineralizing compounds in solution. By way of confirmation, no fossil bone has yet been recovered from pediment or piedmont alluvia. The dissected surfaces of Pleistocene or Holocene fluvio-deltaic beds offer equally few opportunities for rapid burial and mineralization. In fact, ferromagnesian minerals are intensively corroded well below the surface (F. H. Brown, pers. comm.), and both the Vertisol dynamism and the subsurface accumulations of sodium salts indicate that long-term emergence of nonfunctional deposits favors the destruction of all but well-mineralized fossils. Interestingly,

---

[21] Both Pila ovata and exceptionally large specimens of Pila werneri were among modern shells from Sanderson's Gulf identified by Roger (1944).

TABLE 2-5

SUMMARY DATA FOR THE OMO DELTA PLAIN

Geomorphologic Unit	Area (sq. km.)	Characteristic Sediments	Dominant Soils
Meander Belt	175	Sand; silty clay loam	Brown Vega
Eastern Flood Basin	65	Silty clay; clay	Vertisols, Brown Vega
Western Delta Flats	145 ⎫		
Central Delta Flats	35 ⎬ 365	Clay; silty clay; silty clay loam	Vertisols, Brown Vega
Southern Delta Flats	185 ⎭		
Delta Fringe	ca. 400	Clay; silty clay; silty clay loam	Vertisols, Brown Vega
Beach Ridge Plains	ca. 450	Sand, loamy sand; sandy loam	Non-calcic Burozem
Murle Lake Plain	135	*	**
Sanderson's Gulf	750	Clay; clay loam	Vertisols, Non-calcic Burozem

*Probably sandy loams, silty clay loams and clays.

**Include Non-calcic Burozems, Brown Vegas and Vertisols.

however, shell from Holocene members of the Kibish Formation is seldom decalcified, while preservation of partly-decalcified shell or shell impressions in certain Pleistocene or Pliocene beds is comparatively good.

Active sedimentation is optimal in the floodplains, deltas and littoral environments.

The channel sands and silts of the Omo River now contain organic detritus such as fish, reptile or mammal bone, animal droppings and waterlogged tree flotsam, while bird and insect tracks were observed on freshly emerged mud films. Bone preservation is probably good. Mammals watering along the banks are repeatedly snatched by crocodiles, and sudden bank-caving of undercut meander bends will occasionally sweep trees and animals into the river during flood stage. No mollusca were observed in the Omo channel, due to high water, but the freshwater Nile oyster (Etheria elliptica) appears to afix itself onto compacted bed shoals. Although crocodile slide marks may be common and persistent along levee banks, no bone or mollusca were observed at the surface or in sections of levees and other overbank silts. The backswamps of the Eastern Flood Basin are frequented by many birds and mammals of various sizes, but it is doubtful that burial and fossilization occur.

In the Omo Delta proper, the distributary channels presumably form suitable depositional environments comparable to the floodplain channel. Interdistributary environments are less likely to be fossiliferous, although there will certainly be exceptions in vegetated, aquatic settings. On the other hand, the turbid Omo waters that flow into the prodeltaic zone lack the competence to carry bone, let alone coarse sands. Consequently fossils should be limited to fish, reptiles and hippopotamus, except for occasional drifting, bloated cadavers (see De Heinzelin et al., 1971). Silicified wood that is frequently found in certain exposures of the Kibish Formation was probably derived from burial of water-logged driftwood at the head of Lake Rudolf.

The low wave-energy littorals are fringed by aquatic plants today used for cattle grazing, with the animals standing up to their chests in water. Fish such as the Nile perch are also speared in suitable parts of this meso-environment. Bottom sediments consist of only a thin layer of mud, resting on well-sorted, partly arcosic quartz sands of fluvial origin. Fluctuations of this setting, with some fluvio-lacustrine interactions and accumulations of low beach ridges, produce sedimentary sequences of sandy loams and loamy sands, identical to many of the fossiliferous units of the Omo Beds. Because elephants were similarly observed feeding among aquatic grasses in 1888 (Höhnel, 1894: 110, 149), such deposits may well be expected to be fossiliferous. The high wave-energy shores of Lake Rudolf are formed by beach ridges or bars of coarse sand, including gravel near the mouths of major tributaries. Although no modern molluscan communities have been observed along the Rudolf coasts, possibly as a result of the alkalinity of the lake, the sandy shell beds of the fossil record most probably represent foreshores on comparatively high wave-energy littorals. The same applies to some of the fish beds described from the Turkana littoral by Thompson (1966).

Finally, none of the meso-settings in Sanderson's Gulf appears favorable to fossilization and there is now no trace of the fish, reptile and mammal bones seen by Champion (1937) in the Lomogol Delta and attributed to recent desiccation of the "Gulf." It is equally unlikely that fossilization occurs on any of the other active mudflats of the upland plains.

CHAPTER 3

HISTORICAL EVIDENCE FOR RECENT SUBMERGENCE

AND EMERGENCE OF THE DELTA PLAIN

> Fast überall am See sieht man
> gebleichte Baumskelette, die im
> seichten Uferwasser stehen. Am
> auffallendsten ist diese Erscheinung
> einer ertränkten Waldvegetation am
> Nordende des Sees, da sie dort in
> einer 35 km langen Reihe abgestor-
> bener Bäume besteht, die sich vom
> Ufer aus in den See erstreckt.
> --Ludwig Höhnel, 1890

> Les fondrières qui s'étendent fort
> loin vers le nord et de nombreux
> squelettes de poissons font consta-
> ter la régression des eaux du lac.
> --Robert du Bourg de Bozas, 1903

> I had long suspected that there were
> two annual lake levels, a wet
> weather and a dry weather level.
> However, in addition to this yearly
> change of level, there also appears
> to be a marked diminishment of the
> lake.
> --Chauncy Stigand, 1910.

The Sources

Few studies in recent geomorphology have attempted to utilize historical sources
to complement physical evidence or serve as a method of dating. In most instances, of
course, either the rates of change are too slow or the phenomena themselves are next to
impossible to record by either maps or descriptions. But there have also been notable
exceptions, among them the several studies of changing coastlines in the Rhine-Maas-
Schelde estuary and the Frisian Islands since Medieval times, or the Mississippi subdeltas in Louisiana since the 4th century A.D. (see, for example, Fisk, 1952). Surprisingly
enough, despite the remoteness of the Omo Delta, there is a considerable body of literature that allows valuable geomorphologic inferences for the past hundred years.

Successive travellers in the Rudolf region have commented on shoreline features and configuration, drawn sketch maps of varying detail and accuracy, or recorded incidental information on local vegetation or occupance that can be evaluated in the context of geomorphologic evidence outlined in chapter 2. Of particular value were (a) data that allow a reconstruction of the delta topography and (b) notes on submergence or emergence underway. The few attempts to estimate fluctuations of lake level are of limited value since there was no datum that successive travellers could refer to. For these reasons the subsequent analysis must attempt to evaluate the available information in an organic way. The configuration of the delta shorelines is determined as accurately as possible for certain periods, with successive reports utilized to assess positive or negative trends of lake level. Only then can this material be interpreted in terms of approximate elevations and in the light of the geomorphologic field evidence.

Lake Levels prior to 1888. Höhnel visited Lake Rudolf during what appears to have been an exceptionally dry year: no rain fell in Turkana during the spring of 1888 (Höhnel, 1890) and Nile discharge was the lowest for the period 1871-98 (see U. S. Dept. of Commerce, 1959: 1325). However, the coastal evidence indicates that the lake level had been rising over the previous few years. In Alia Bay, large native villages were found on two low sandbanks some 200 meters offshore (Höhnel, 1894: 132f.), i.e. on a partly-submerged beach ridge. Along the southeastern shores there were numerous groups of dead trees (including dum palms) standing in shallow water, or at and just above the watermark (Höhnel, 1894: 97, 133). These trees presumably were killed off by the rise of alkaline lake and ground waters. Similarly, Höhnel (1894: 151, 156, 159f.; also Höhnel, 1890; Höhnel et al., 1891: 20) described and illustrated a string of widely spaced, dead tree trunks that once formed an extension of the Omo River and extended, half-submerged, for almost 35 kilometers[1] out into the lake. This once had been a fringing woodland that extended along drowned levees. In other words, at some time prior to 1888 the lake had been appreciably lower for a sufficiently long time to permit mature trees to grow. Since the trees were widely spaced, bleached, and rather spindly in appearance it seems safe to assume that submergence had begun at least a decade earlier,[2] during the early 1870's.

---

[1] Given as 15 miles (24 km) by Höhnel (1938: 26f.) who noted that "the further this tree line went from the shore the more decayed were the trees and the more sparse the row."

[2] In 1968 a number of dead fig trees could be seen along the Erdete and Dielerhiele Branches, among the levee woodland. These appear to have died in response to the rising water level since 1961, and in one instance death had occurred during the previous 3 years. This suggests that total destruction of a fringing woodland along several tens of kilometers of channel length would take at the very least a decade--in the case of a very rapid rise of level--and, more probably, several decades.

Finally, the development of a fringing woodland would seem to require a minimum of three to five decades,[3] suggesting that the previous period of low lake level lasted 50 years or more.

Hohnel also noted sporadic indications of former higher lake levels. Near the southern end of Alia Bay there were numerous catfish in rain pools at some distance from the shore (Höhnel, 1894: 212f.), presumably indicating a seasonal drop or short-term negative oscillation of Lake Rudolf. Somewhat older are the Etheria encrustations seen on rocks about +20 or 30 meters[4] near the southeastern corner of Rudolf (Höhnel et al., 1891: 20), and the dry salt pans at +10 meters, separated from the shore by a low sand ridge, found a little further north (Höhnel, 1894: 113). Allowing for a +8- to 10-meter lake level in 1888 (see below), these beach features may record the +20- and +30-meter shorelines of Lake Rudolf.

March to May, 1888. Topography at the head of Lake Rudolf during the spring of 1888 can be reconstructed on the basis of Höhnel's (1890, 1894) 1:750,000 map and with reference to the location of Teleki's camp site.

Despite some distortions in shape and width, Höhnel's map can be superimposed on the current 1:1 million series and several salient headlands and bays identified. Near the delta, the great alluvial fan of the Macho Afas is unmistakable and provides orientation. Teleki's camp was located on a ridge of white sand running parallel to the lake shore (Höhnel, 1894: 151, 160.; 1938), separated from the riverine forest of the Omo levees by an open stretch of water a kilometer or so across (Höhnel, 1894: 202 and folding map). As the river level rose, water flooded back into this embayment and eventually doubled around the end of the sand ridge to form a lake in the depression east of the camp (Höhnel, 1894: 202; Höhnel, 1938). Smith (1896) visited the site in 1895, and determined coordinates[5] that can be located on Smith's map and thereby permit an identification not possible from Höhnel's map alone. On this basis there can be little doubt that Teleki's camp site was situated near the western end of the Nargi Ridge (E2b/3) (see Fig. 2-2), at 4°48'23±2''N, 36°6'49±2''E.

---

[3] Mature trees, although no mature forest (Carr, n.d.), developed along the lowermost Omo River (e.g. Subdeltas A2 and B3) between 1933 (see Arambourg, 1944: 189) and the 1960's.

[4] Rendered as 50-60 feet (15-18m) in the Bell translation (Höhnel, 1894: 105), and variably given as 60 and 100 feet (18-30m) in Höhnel (1938: 23 and 44).

[5] Somewhat inaccurately stated as 4°45'N and 36°7'15''E. Höhnel (1890) gives the latitude as 4°42'15''N, but since he had lost much of his surveying equipment, most of his coordinates in the Rudolf area are equally inaccurate.

Interpreting Höhnel's map with these clues, it is possible to reconstruct the delta plain as shown by Fig. 3-1. The eastern and western shorelines of Rudolf follow the foot of the W3b-E2b beach ridges. The Omo channel with the submerged levee woodland is a little problematical to identify but the evidence favors an association with the modern Omo River upstream of and extending into Subdelta B3.[6] The existence of a large body of overbank water in the Eastern Flood Basin is beyond question since Höhnel (1894: 203ff.) traversed this area on his way to the Bume village. Information for the western delta is scanty, however, since Höhnel was not allowed to cross the Omo. Conflicting hearsay evidence indicated the presence of either or both a running river or a broad and shallow embayment, a few kilometers wide and with practically no current (Höhnel et al., 1891: 19; Höhnel, 1938). Known as Bass, or "water," this information almost certainly referred to a lagoon of uncertain dimensions extending into the Western Delta Flats.

The configuration of the Omo mouth in Fig. 3-1 is compatible with that given by Höhnel (see Fig. 3-1, inset). The presence of a mighty galeria forest with lianas and adjacent thickets (Höhnel, 1894: 202) presumably obscured further topographic details.[7] By contrast, the vegetation to the east and north was open, with scattered bush and umbrella acacias[8] on the sandy tracts, while the flood lowlands were overgrown with shrub vegetation and intersected by channels (Höhnel, 1894: 160, 201). These notations on the vegetation are eminently reasonable in the light of modern patterns, and increase confidence in the general physical description left of the Omo Delta in 1888.

In overview, the northern end of the open lake terminated near 4°48'N in 1888, and the shoreline was just at or, better, a little below that of the 10-meter stage, indicating a lake level 8 to 10 meters higher than that of 1970. It seems probable that the preceding higher stand (+15 meters?) can be dated in the late 1870's and early '80's, although Lake Rudolf can have been no higher than now during the mid-19th century.

July, 1895 to October, 1896. A rise of Lake Rudolf during the mid-1890's was documented in the course of successive visits by Donaldson Smith (mid-July to early August,

---

[6] See Fig. 2-2, where this channel coincides most closely with the line of trees drawn on Höhnel's map. Fuchs in a footnote to Höhnel (1938: 27, No. 1) concludes that Höhnel was not referring to the promontory of high ground that converges on the new fort of Namuruputh.

[7] Höhnel (1938: 25) admits as much with "Some of our men had been there fishing (on the Nianam = Omo River) long before we ourselves saw it (from the camp site), which was not until the rainy season had set in. We then found the Nianam . . . flowing . . . through dense forest growth."

[8] Probably the Acacia tortilis now found on the Nargi Ridge (see Carr, n.d.).

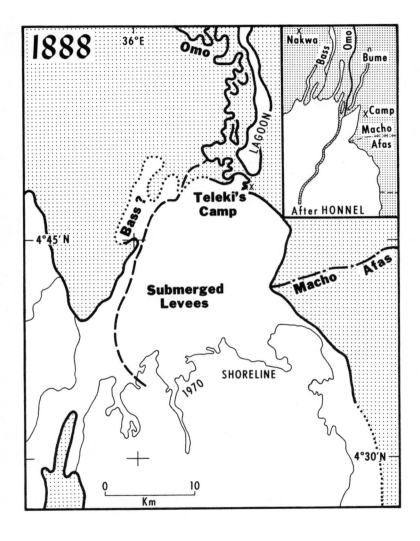

Fig. 3-1. Reconstruction of the Omo Delta in 1888. Inset shows Höhnel's rendition as published 1894.

1895),[9] Arthur Neumann (mid-December, 1895 to mid-April, 1896)[10] and the Bòttego Expedition (late August to mid-December, 1896).

In July, 1895, Teleki's camp site had been largely inundated and the nearby village described by Höhnel had been abandoned in favor of higher ground.[11] Furthermore, the offshore beach ridges at Alia Bay had been submerged. Smith (1896) documented the coastal configuration on a 1:1 million map (see Fig. 3-2 inset) that shows a slight but significant transgression of Lake Rudolf. The Eastern Flood Plain was directly connected to the open lake by a narrow sound and the Nargi Beach Ridge formed a conspicuous and extensive sector of the shore. In fact the coastline east of the Omo embouchure coincides with the E2b or E3 beach ridges. A 20-kilometer tract of "marsh" is indicated where Höhnel had recorded his submerged levee woodland, but this feature is not described in the accompanying text. No river was found west of the Omo but a small embayment is shown on the map. The western delta margins remained unexplored.

All the evidence indicates that in mid-July, 1895, the lake was at or just below the 15-meter line of the E3 beach ridges, the Omo River terminating at about 4°51'N. Lake level was therefore about 5 meters higher than in 1888.

The rise of the lake had reduced much of the Delta woodland to a swamp forest infested with mosquitoes, and it was next to impossible for Neumann (1898) to delineate the shoreline. At any rate his 1:1.9 million map is highly generalized as well as adapted from the charts of Höhnel and Smith, so that its value is limited. However, Neumann (1898: 294) now found the Bume living in "a few kraals scattered at intervals along the lake, " near the northern end of a bay extending up the Eastern Flood Basin,[12] whereas Höhnel (1894: 203f.) had found their palisaded village on the Omo levee in 1888; clearly the settlements are not identical, reducing their value as landmarks but suggesting a shift of settlement in response to the lake transgression.

The Bòttego Expedition provided the first reasonable map of the head of Lake Rudolf through exploration of the eastern delta plain in late August and October, and the

---

[9] Smith (1896) reached the Omo Delta from Somalia, travelled up the east bank of the Omo and then along the lower Usno (which he mistook for the Omo). He returned south by the eastern shores of Rudolf. His travelling companion, a Mr. Dodson, skirted part of the delta coast with a portable boat.

[10] Neumann (1898) travelled to and from the Omo region, where he spent two months of enforced convalescence due to a hunting mishap, by the east Rudolf route.

[11] Instead the "water (was) high up among the bushes" (Smith, 1896: 227).

[12] Because they travelled north along the eastern side of this bay and via the Bume settlement directly to Murle, neither Smith nor Neumann passed the Shungura Meander Belt and so missed the great bends of the Omo River below Murle (see their maps).

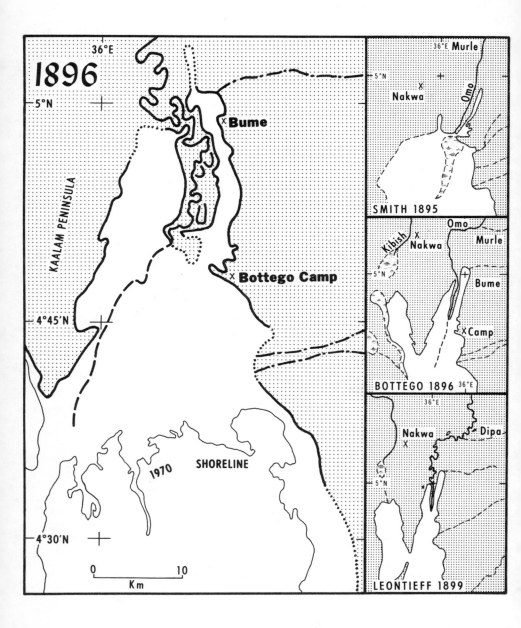

Fig. 3-2. Reconstruction of the Omo Delta in 1896. Insets show the outlines and latitudes given by Smith (1896), Vannutelli and Citerni (1899), and Léontieff (1900), reduced to comparable scales.

western delta, much of Sanderson's Gulf, as well as the Kibish River in November and early December of 1896 (Vannutelli and Citerni, 1899: chaps. 12-14). Although the Bòttego elevations and meridians of longitude are not exact, the final latitudinal determinations are quite reliable and the 1:1 million map provides a useful base for reconstructing the delta topography in 1896 (Fig. 3-2). Particularly fortunate are a number of coastal indentations that can be identified with particular beach ridges. The critical areas and key locations can be discussed as follows:

(a) The terminus of the Omo River (stage 3a) was at the modern Omo-Murdizi bifurcation, according to Bòttego's latitude (4°51'N) and with reference to the adjacent W4 and E3 beach ridges. At the same time a line of swamp symbols project the Omo as far as latitude 4°40'N, opposite the Lomogol and Macho Afas embouchures. This is the same submerged levee woodland seen by Höhnel in 1888 and identified with Stage 2 of the Murdizi Branch.

(b) The Nargi Beach Ridge is prominent, with Bòttego's camp located at 4°48'N, near the crest.[13] The several coastal indentations just to the north can be recognized on the air photos where they correspond to drainage swales and terminate with the next E3 beach promontory.

(c) The tip of the Kaalam Peninsula, to the west, is shown at 4°41'N, coinciding with the southern end of the W4a beach ridge. This is corroborated by the two spits on the eastern side of the peninsula that can be identified with the W4 and W5 ridges. The W3 ridges are not in evidence and must have been submerged.

(d) At the opposite, southern entrance to Sanderson's Gulf there is no indication of the W1 beach ridge, even though Bòttego returned from Turkana along the immediate shore and would almost certainly have seen such a feature. Interestingly enough, all later maps (since 1897, e.g. Cavendish, 1898) show this spit.[14] There seems no reason to doubt that the W1 ridge, with dunes and adjacent outcrops of older formations--in 1968 found at +7 to 15 meters--was submerged in 1896. At that time the lake waters certainly reached their highest mark since 1888, and possibly their maximum level since well over a century.

(e) The embayment in the Eastern Flood Plain extends to 5°03'N and is described as swampy (Vannutelli and Citerni, 1899: 329). Later authors indicate a projection of water to the northern extremity of this plain, which Bòttego may not have seen. The Bume village, then organized in a circular arrangement, appears to have been situated on the northernmost E3 beach ridge, with strips of cultivation along the lakeshore (Vannutelli and Citerni, 1899: 329). The village site is corroborated with reference to the large, intermittent stream a little to the north.

(f) Another embayment extended to the northern end of the Western Delta Flats (4°57'N). The coastal configuration is rendered schematically by Bòttego, who did not pass along the shore and whose view was presumably obscured by marsh vegetation.

(g) Sanderson's Gulf extended to 4°56'N but only as far west as 35°55'E, in other words only the cracking clays of the central and southern mudflats were submerged.

---

[13] The Italians stayed in a hut built by Smith a year earlier (Vannutelli and Citerni, 1899: 335). Amusingly, they found an English newspaper of 1894 inside.

[14] Although neither Smith (1896) nor Neumann (1898) traversed the western shoreline, it may be significant that their maps give no indication of the existence of such a spit in 1895-96.

A large tract of dry ground is indicated between the gulf waters and the marshland of the Kibish Delta, and the Kibish River did not connect with the lake. The low tracts of the northwestern "Gulf" are indicated as marsh (see Fig. 3-2, inset). This relatively conservative view of the degree of submergence in Sanderson's Gulf appears quite reasonable in view of the geomorphologic expression, and is confirmed by a number of later maps.

(h) Finally, the major alignment of the Omo River corresponds to that of the present, although meanders are only hinted at by schematic sinuosity. The Murle village, which has since disappeared, was situated east of the great bend near Lake Dipa, just south of a large eastern tributary, at about 5°10'N. On Nov. 5, 1896, the river was found to be 4 meters deep and 200 meters wide at the Murle ford (Vannutelli and Citerni, 1899: 362).

In sum, Bòttego's map provides a great amount of detail that is internally consistent and compatible with the field evidence.[15] There can be little question that the shoreline coincided with the E3 beach ridges to the east, the W4a ridges to the west. At the same time, the W1 ridge complex was submerged by a lake at least 15 meters higher than today. The full weight of the evidence implies that Lake Rudolf climaxed at +15 meters or a little higher during the autumn of 1896.

Records from 1897 to 1903. Following Bòttego's study of the delta, some 11 individuals or expedition groups visited the northern Rudolf area in rapid succession: H. S. H. Cavendish and H. Andrew in late March and early April, 1897 (Cavendish, 1898);[16] A. K. Bulatovich in early April, 1898 (Bulatovich, 1900);[17] H. H. Austin in September, 1898 (Austin, 1899);[18] M. S. Wellby in early March, 1899 (Wellby, 1900);[19] N. de Léontieff from late August to early October 1899 (Leontieff, 1900);[20] Donaldson Smith between mid-

---

[15] Unfortunately the primary publications of the Bòttego Expedition were not readily accessible, and were not consulted by later travellers except for Léontieff (1900). Neither did the British cartography profit from Bòttego's topographic information and subsequent maps, until the 1908 survey of Gwynn (1911), are vastly inferior. Even Fuchs' bibliography (in Höhnel, 1938) cites no specific publications of the Italian expedition, and it is apparent that Höhnel (1938) did not use the final report of Vannutelli and Citerni (1899) for his own review of the early visitors.

[16] Cavendish travelled across from Lake Stefanie to Murle and continued around Sanderson's Gulf and down the western shores of Rudolf, while Andrew took the eastern route (Cavendish, 1898).

[17] Bulatovich accompanied an Ethiopian military mission under Wolde Giyorgis to the western delta margins, via Maji (Bulatovich, 1900). His text, unnecessarily and abusively footnoted by Roncagli, is only of historical interest while his generalized 1:2.8 million map is vaguely reminiscent of Bòttego's in the delta area.

[18] On his first trip Austin (1899) traversed Turkana and the western delta region.

[19] Wellby (1900) travelled rapidly down the eastern margins of the delta and lake, on his way from Addis Ababa to Kenya.

[20] Léontieff, a Russian count, completed the Ethiopian conquest of the lower Omo Val-

December, 1899 and mid-January, 1900 (Smith, 1900);[21] J. J. Harrison and his party in late March and early April, 1900 (Harrison, 1901);[22] Austin in April, 1901 (Austin, 1902);[23] the Bourg de Bozas Expedition in June, 1902 (Bourg de Bozas, 1903);[24] Philip Maud and a British surveying group in May, 1903 (Maud, 1904);[25] and J. W. Brooke and his party in late 1903 (Brooke, 1905).[26] The value of these reports varies considerably, some contributing descriptions of the countryside, some on the peoples, and others recounting little but the petty details of day-to-day travel. Höhnel (1938) provides a useful resume of most of these authors.

Although Cavendish's (1898) map of the delta region is taken directly from Smith (1895), the sketch of Sanderson's Gulf was original and shows the presence of a complex spit at the southern entrance to the gulf--only 4 months after Bòttego's visit. The irregularity of this spit is not repeated by later maps and suggests that only a few dune lines and higher crests were emergent. Cavendish interpreted the gulf littorals as "recently emerged lake bottom," and appears to have been witness to a rapid seasonal drop of lake level during the winter of 1896-97, possibly of as much as 2 meters.[27] It is probably significant that Cavendish is the last author to indicate a marshy zone corresponding to Höhnel's submerged levee woodland.

---

ley and arrived at Lake Rudolf Aug. 21, 1899, via the western bank of the Omo. He then invaded Turkana, turning back south of the Kerio River Oct. 1, 1899 (see Léontieff, 1900).

[21] Smith's second trip largely retraced the steps of his first travels east of the delta, after which he followed the Omo and then crossed over towards the middle Kibish River (Smith, 1900).

[22] Harrison (1901) visited only the eastern delta region.

[23] His second trip took Austin (1902) across the Kibish plains to the Murle country.

[24] The leader Count Robert du Bourg de Bozas, died of malaria before this transcontinental expedition reached the Atlantic coast. Many or most of the scientific observations must be credited to Emile Brumpt, who served as doctor and naturalist, and later became professor of parasitology at Paris. It was he who discovered the fossiliferous Omo Beds and recognized their significance by bringing back a valuable collection of fossils (see Arambourg, 1944-48). The major publication of the expedition, edited by Saint-Arroman (1906), is merely a travelog.

[25] Maud (1904) surveyed the borderlands between Ethiopia, Kenya and Sudan, demarcating one of two proposed frontiers between Ethiopian and British interests. Yet his report as such is a travelog of little interest.

[26] The British East Africa Syndicate's expedition, of which Brooke was a member, visited only the western margins of the lake and delta (see Brooke, 1905).

[27] However, this would not be compatible with an Omo current of 3 or 4 knots (!) in March (see Cavendish, 1897).

Austin's (1899) 1:2.5 million map is too generalized to provide any details, e.g. on beach ridges or on the Omo channels. But it does show that the broad coastal configuration was the same in 1898 as in 1896, except for the continued emergence of the W1 ridge at Todenyang. The Rudolf embayment in the Eastern Floodplain terminated at 5° 03'N, that in the Western Delta Flats at 4° 57'N, and the tip of the Kaalam Peninsula was at 4° 41'N, while Sanderson's Gulf extended to 4° 56'N--all values identical to those of Bòttego. The length of the gulf was given as 58 kilometers (36 mi), the width as about 10 kilometers (6-7 mi). Submerged vegetation was seen extensively along the western shores of Rudolf, with a line of trees extending "between 2 and 3 miles out into the lake." In general, the lake shoreline must have fluctuated at and a little below +15 meters through 1897-98.

Wellby (1900) simply repróduced Austin's map. However he found the Omo at Murle narrowed down to 30 yards with "scarcely any appreciable current" in March, 1899, whereas Austin estimated channel width at 100 to 150 yards the following September.

The most surprising of the late 19th century maps is the 1:1.5 million chart of Léontieff (1900), which accurately depicts all the major meanders of the Omo River between the Usno confluence and the Shungura Meander Belt (see Fig. 3-2, inset). Both Lakes Lokulat and Dipa were already cut-off as oxbow lakes in April, 1899. The two oxbows of the Shungura belt are not shown; instead, the river followed its present course. No details are given for the Narok sector, and the delta coastal configuration is identical to that of Bòttego, except that the entire western Delta Flats are shown to be submerged. The W1 beach ridge is conspicuous at the south end of Sanderson's Gulf. Léontieff's rendition of the Omo channel configuration remained unique until the 1930's[28] and shows conclusively that Stage 3b reflects the channel geometry of the late 19th century.

The persistence in 1899-1900 of partly-submerged riverine vegetation along the Omo River as far south as latitude 4°46'N is verified by Smith's (1900) 1:2 million map. This chart shows that the Eastern Flood Plain remained submerged but otherwise contributes little new, duplicating Austin (1899) for Sanderson's Gulf but at a grossly exaggerated scale. Without giving details for his conclusions, Smith states that the lake level was 3.6 meters lower in January, 1900 than in August, 1895. A regression of 3.6 meters from the maximum of 1895-96 to the winter of 1899-1900 appears reasonable. On March 31, 1900, Harrison (1901) found the Omo channel at Murle completely dry and covered with fresh grass.[29] He also noted striking signs of a falling lake level: "On carefully examin-

---

[28]Geographical coordinates for the map are indirectly attributed to a Dr. Kahn, the French doctor accompanying Léontieff. Presumably the cartography owes much or all to his staff of French mercenaries. Unfortunately Léontieff's informative account remained unnoticed by later writers and the one author to use his work (Pauli, 1950) gives a wrong citation.

[29]There are no secondary channels of the Omo near the site of the former Murle

ing Rudolf, we found its level had sunk 12 feet during the last year, while in what appeared as three stages (no doubt years) the lake had lost 28 feet" (Harrison, 1901: 273). The critical value of 3.6 meters substantiates Smith. Nonetheless, Rudolf cannot possibly have dropped 8.5 meters 1897-1900 and Harrison must have mistaken some of the E4 ridge features (i.e., the "20-meter" shoreline) to be subcontemporary. However, there is little reason to doubt a falling lake level as of 1900. The years 1898-1900 saw an unprecedented drought across the whole of East Africa to the Nile (Harrison, 1901; Austin, 1902), and the Nile volume for 1899 was the lowest since the beginning of records in 1871 (see U.S. Dept. of Commerce, 1959: 1325), with discharge remaining abnormally low through 1907.

By April, 1901, the recession of Lake Rudolf was apparent. The water was more alkaline than usual, and numerous lagoons once teeming with wildfowl were largely dry (Austin, 1902). In June of 1902 this condition was accentuated, with fish skeletons litter-ing former lake beds. In fact, the relatively poor 1:2 million map of Bourg de Bozas (1903)[30] shows that the northern parts of both the Eastern Flood Plain and the Western Delta Flats (to about 4° 55'N) were dry, while the Omo terminated near or just a little north of Narok. Sanderson's Gulf and the Kibish Delta are indicated by small tracts of marshland, so that all but the southernmost third of the "Gulf" was emergent--no northern embayment is shown. Consequently the shoreline configuration in June 1902 can be tentatively recon-structed on the basis of Bourg de Bozas' (1903) data: east of the delta the shoreline appar-ently coincided with the E2b beaches (+10 meters), while to the west the W2a and W2b ridges were submerged (+3 to 3.5 meters). This suggests that the lake level was between 5 and 10 meters higher than today.

Although Maud (1904) provided a fairly accurate, original map of the Omo River north of Murle, the surprising fact is that as chief surveyor of a border triangulation he did not visit the delta. His 1:2 million map, which shows the lake at 5° 01'N, is unreliable since the delta topography was drawn by an assistant surveyor from a distant point on the eastern shore of the lake (see comments by Gwynn, 1911). The outline of Sanderson's Gulf was obviously copied from Austin's 1899 map. Later the same year Brooke (1905) vis-ited the area but his map simply duplicates that of Austin (1902). Consequently there is no satisfactory data on the extent of regression in the delta and Sanderson's Gulf as of 1903.

In overview, it seems that Lake Rudolf had reached a maximum level in 1895-96, but dropped rapidly during the winter of 1896-97--by as much as 2 meters. A further decline during 1899-1900, apparently linked to a drastic diminution of Omo discharge, brought the level of April, 1900, to 3.5 meters below that of 1896. Indirect evidence of

---

village and there is no reason whatsoever to doubt the veracity of Harrison's report, as does Höhnel (1938).

[30]But at least original, thus inspiring more confidence than the duplicates of Austin (1899) given by Wellby (1900), Austin (1902), the 1:1 million map of the War Office (1903), Maud (1904) and Brooke (1905).

widespread emergence in the delta suggests that the lake dropped further through 1902, when the level was at least 5 meters lower than in 1896.

Records from 1904 to 1921. Visitors to the Omo Delta were few after 1903. They include C. W. Gwynn in late February and early March, 1908 (Gwynn, 1911);[31] G. Escherich in May, 1909 (Escherich, 1921);[32] C. H. Stigand in mid-1909 (Stigand, 1910);[33] W. P. Holland in May, 1918 and again in 1921 (Holland, 1926);[34] and L. F. I. Athill in April, 1919 (Athill, 1920).[35] The long break from 1910 to 1917 presumably reflects on the tribal unrest and Ethiopian intervention in northern Turkana, as a result of which the borderlands were effectively closed to travellers. The British "pacification" of Turkana, begun in 1914 and terminated 1926 (see Gulliver and Gulliver, 1953: 54), restricted observation in the northern Rudolf area to British officers, and even thereafter travellers were discouraged or precluded from Turkana. The Ethiopian border itself remained closed until the outbreak of World War II, with notable exception of Arambourg's expedition in 1932-33.

The survey of Gwynn (1911) provides a vital marker in the recent history of the Omo Delta. His 1:2 million map and the terse, accompanying description allow a reconstruction of the delta configuration in 1908 (Fig. 3-3). He used a different map pattern to show the "twilight" zone of the delta that Maud (1904) had indicated as water but which was under cultivation in 1908. Marsh symbols are used in Fig. 3-3 to designate these recently emerged lowlands since, as Gwynn (1911: 124f) puts it: "There were several small lagoons near the river which probably increase greatly in area when the Omo rises, but the general

[31]Gwynn (1911) carried out the second attempt at a border demarcation between Kenya and Ethiopia during 1908-09, and visited the lower Omo valley more extensively than Maud.

[32]Escherich (1921) came down to the delta during the course of a hunting expedition that left Addis Ababa in March, 1909, returning there in July of the same year. Apart from a useful, current description of the lower Omo region, the comments on game and the poaching problem are valuable.

[33]Stigand (1910) travelled up the eastern shores of Lake Rudolf to the delta and then upstream to Kerre.

[34]Holland (1926), an officer in northern Turkana, did not cross the border into Ethiopia, but made his observations from the western shores of Sanderson's Gulf. His notes on volcanic activity in the Kaalam area are wholly erroneous and the phenomena he observed must be attributed to grass fires, as Arambourg (1943: 180) has already pointed out.

[35]Athill (1920) left a fascinating account as the senior British representative on a joint Ethiopian-British demarcation of the borderlands in southwestern Ethiopia and the adjacent Sudan.

117

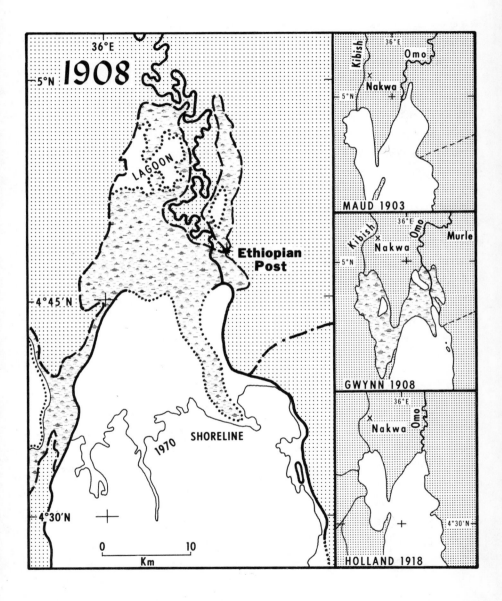

Fig. 3-3. Reconstruction of the Omo Delta in 1908. Insets show maps published by Maud (1904), Gwynn (1911), and Holland (1926).

characteristics of the vegetation were those of marshland, not dry lake bottom. It is in any case impossible to define the limits of the lake by a hard-and-fast line. " As shown, the 1908 shoreline runs along the foot of the E1, W3a, and W2a/2b beach ridges, leaving the Southern Delta Flats submerged. The water level can therefore be estimated at 2 or 2.5 meters above that of 1970, i.e. 12 or 13 meters lower than in 1896. Since Gwynn did not visit Sanderson's Gulf, the extent of submergence there remains conjectural, although the "gulf" was evidently cut off from the open lake.

Particularly interesting are the tongue of land projecting into Lake Rudolf for almost 15 kilometers and the two small islands off the eastern shore. The location of this projection, with reference to "landmarks" on both adjacent coasts, coincides exactly with the central Murdizi River. Although reminiscent of Höhnel's submerged levee woodland of 1888, the map orientation of the feature shown by Höhnel (1888), Smith (1896), and Vannutelli and Citerni (1899) is 75° different to that of Gwynn's tongue of land, i.e. southwesterly instead of south-southeasterly. The two islets (Fig. 3-3) coincide with other segments of the Murdizi levees, also prominent today. By implication, the downwarped zone at the entrance to Lake Fadja was already present. This suggests strongly that the central and lower Murdizi channel and its associated depositional features are indicated by the discontinuous line of higher ground on Gwynn's map. This seems to show that the lower Murdizi and its subdeltas predate the submergence of the 19th century, with the levee woodland that once existed here destroyed well before Höhnel's visit in 1888. Although at least one of the Omo mouths in 1908 coincided with the uppermost Murdizi River, it should be emphasized that no source in the 20th century gives any indication that the Murdizi subdeltas were functional or that the Omo followed the central and lower parts of the Murdizi channel trace. With this perspective, Gwynn's representation provides the key evidence for the antiquity of the Murdizi system.

The comments of Escherich and Stigand add confirmation to the fall of lake level during the decade preceding 1909. Escherich (1921: 127) found the Omo turbid in mid-May, and flowing in an incised channel over 200 meters in width. Reed and sedge swamps were extensive in the lower delta reaches, with reeds and occasional groups of dead trees above the flat, sandy shore (Escherich, 1921: 136, 143f.). Stigand (1910: 179) noted miles of dry, cracked mud along the southeastern shores of Lake Rudolf, and found that the beach ridge on which the Elmolo of Alia Bay had been settled in 1888 was no longer submerged, as in 1895, but situated a kilometer inland (Stigand, 1910: 192).[36]

The years 1917-18 were unusually wet in western Ethiopia, judging by a Sobat River discharge 58 to 73% higher than the 1912-1957 average (see Hurst and Phillips, 1935:

---

[36] Stigand's estimate (1910: 179) that the lake had recently fallen by 6 to 8 ft (1.8-2.4m) may relate to the change in level since 1902 or 1903.

186f.), and the Kibish River flowed past Nakwa all year in 1917 (Worthington, 1932). It is therefore not surprising to find that Lake Rudolf flooded 2.5 kilometers up the mouth of the Kabua River, and had reestablished an open sound with Sanderson's Gulf in 1918 (Holland, 1926). Holland's 1:1 million map for 1918 finds confirmation for the western delta in Athill's (1920) comparable but original 1:4 million chart for 1919. From both it can be inferred that a 7-kilometer stretch of open water linked Rudolf to Sanderson's Gulf. The W2a/2b beach ridges were submerged, except for their superposed dunes, while the W3a ridges formed the shoreline of the Kaalam Peninsula. The tip of the latter was at latitude 4°38'N, the northern terminus of Sanderson's Gulf at 4°55'N according to Holland, at 4°48'N according to Athill (1920), who implies recent desiccation of the peripheral sectors. Accordingly Lake Rudolf must have been 4 to 5 meters higher than today in 1918-19, indicating a 2 or 3 meter rise in level during World War I. [37]

The high stand apparent in 1918-19 was short-lived. By 1921 the lake level had fallen so much that the stumps of dum palms, not visible in 1918, now averaged 3 to 3.5 meters high on the water edge (Holland, 1926). Consequently the 1921 level was probably 3 to 4 meters below that of 1918-19, i.e. less than 1 meter above that of 1970. The lake may already have been dropping in 1919 so that the transgression probably climaxed in 1918. The length of this positive oscillation was only 3 or 4 years, its amplitude 3 or 4 meters--all in all a rather striking event.

Records from 1921 to 1960. Although adequately documented in terms of general trends, the record of the 1920's and 1930's is sparse. The only source between 1921 and 1932 is the 1:2 million map compiled early in the 1920's (War Office, 1925: sheet B/C-36/37), and borrowing in part from Gwynn (1911)[38] and Athill (1920) (see Fig. 3-4, inset). There appear to be some original aspects, however. The head of the lake is at 4°43'N, somewhat south of the W3a beach ridge, while the sound to Sanderson's Gulf is narrowed down to less than 3 kilometers, with the tip of the Kaalam Peninsula at 4°37'N. This would indicate that the lake level was slightly below the crest of the W2a/2b beach ridges, little more than 2 meters above the 1970 mark. Presumably military information, from as late as 1923 or 1924, is reflected in this map.

Arambourg (1944) worked west of the Omo Delta between December, 1932, and March, 1933. His attention to the delta itself was incidental, but his 1:500,000 map shows the head of the lake at about 4° 34'N, with Sanderson's Gulf dry and the Omo River bifurcated

---

[37] Somewhat less than the 15-20 ft (4.5-6.0m) suggested by Holland (1926).

[38] The 1920 edition of the London Times Survey Atlas of the World (plate 75) simply duplicates Gwynn (1911).

120

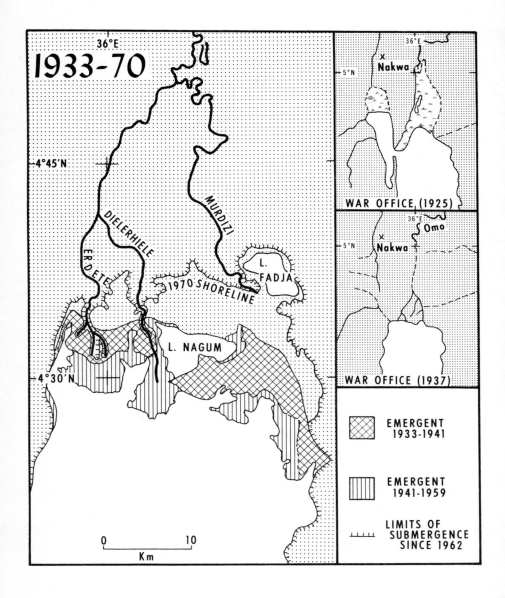

Fig. 3-4. Changes in Delta Topography 1933-1970. Insets show the configuration given by the 1:2 million maps of 1925 and 1937, at identical scales to the insets of Figs. 3-1 to 3-3.

into the Erdete (main) and Dielerhiele (subsidiary) branches (see shoreline location on Fig. 3-4).[39] Arambourg's map is corroborated by a 1:250,000 map compiled in the field by A. M. Champion in 1933 but published at a reduced scale several years later (Champion, 1937).[40] This places the lake in early 1933 lower than in 1967-70, with a shoreline 5 to 10 kilometers further south. Extrapolating the mean gradient of the Southern Delta Flats (about 1m/3km), the lake level would have been 2 meters lower than in 1970.

The years 1932-34 were ones of severe drought in northern Kenya (Champion, 1937), and V. E. Fuchs (1939) estimated a drop in lake level of 0.8 or 0.9 meters between his field seasons of 1931 and 1934 in northern Turkana, while Champion (1937) claimed a drop of at least 30 centimeters per year for the 5 years preceding 1936. The 1:2 million map compiled in the mid-1930's (War Office, 3rd edition 1937) adheres closely to Champion's coastal configuration and rendition of Sanderson's Gulf, but provides useful, additional detail for the delta bifurcations. The Murdizi Branch is schematically shown, without a delta, but with two defunct distributaries (see Fig. 3-4, inset) that can be identified on Fig. 2-2.

The next source is the RAF aerial photography of the winter of 1940-41 which formed the base of the 1:250,000 East Africa Survey map of 1943 (sheet 1497)[41] and subsequent editions of the 1:500,000 world map (War Office, 4th edition 1946: sheets NB 366 and 374). Most striking is the 3- to 6-kilometer recession of Lake Rudolf in the delta since 1933, with the Erdete Subdelta "advancing" 3.5 kilometers, the Dielerhiele Subdelta 4.5 kilometers. This could be explained by a phenomenal progradation rate of about 4 kilometers in 8 years (500m/yr) or, more plausibly, by a falling lake level. The Murdizi subdeltas now appeared for the first time, even though the Murdizi channel itself was nonfunctional.[42] Since the patterns and morphology of these subdeltas--including the zones of subsidence--were already fully established in 1941, they must be considered as emerged, relict, features. Both Lake Fadja and Sanderson's Gulf[43] were dry, but the outlines of

---

[39] Arambourg's biological associates, R. Jeannel (1934: 95ff.) and P. A. Chappuis (1935: 78ff.), contribute little beyond Arambourg's (1944: 186ff.) discussion.

[40] Although Arambourg employed Champion's base map in Turkana and elsewhere, his delta details differ from those of Champion, who was unable to visit the Ethiopian side of the frontier. Champion also placed the Kenya-Sudan border somewhat south (4°34'30"N) of of its correct latitude (4°37'N). A curious anachronism is that the reputable Atlante internazionale del Touring Club Italiano (Milano, 1933-34, plates 116-117) simply reproduced Bòttego's topography.

[41] The writer has not had opportunity to see the photographs except as reflected in this 1:250,000 map.

[42] Labelled as "old dry river bed, well defined."

[43] Labelled respectively as "open, flat featureless country" and "flat, featureless country, liable to flood."

Lake Nagum are apparent. Assuming a gradient of 1m/3km, Rudolf was probably 1.5 meters lower in early 1941 than it was in 1933, i.e. about 3.5 meters below the 1967-70 level.

The aerial photography of February, 1959, gives the delta configuration that was adopted by the 1:100,000 topographic series of Kenya (1961, series Y633, sheets 4a and 5), as shown on Fig. 2-1. The Erdete Subdelta had "advanced" 3 kilometers, the Dielerhiele 6.5 kilometers, suggesting significant progradation of the more active delta arm. In fact, a minimum of 3.5 kilometers in 18 years (200m/yr) must be attributed to sedimentation if the 3-kilometer advance of the Erdete Subdelta is attributed entirely to a further drop of lake level.[44] Such a regression is, in fact, indicated by substantial accretions of land in the Murdizi subdeltas. On the average, excluding the Dielerhiele case, the delta shore-line shifted 1 to 1.5 kilometers, implying a further decline of Lake Rudolf by 0.5 meters since the beginning of 1941. This argument of the Delta Fringe gradients underlies the assumption that Rudolf was 4 meters lower in 1959 than in 1967-70.[45]

Minor fluctuations between 1949 and 1961 are accurately recorded by the gauge readings synthesized in Fig. 1-14. The mean annual lake level was similar from 1949 through early 1953 and 1957[46] to late 1961, but averaged almost 1 meter lower between 1954 and 1956. In other words, Lake Rudolf seems to have reached its lowest point in mid-1954, when the seasonal level was 5.5 meters below the mean of 1967-1970.

The Transgression of 1962. Lake Rudolf rose rapidly at the end of 1961 and well into 1962, partially submerging Fort Wilkinson, near Todenyang (see Fig. 3-5). This fort had been built about 1930,[47] so that the lake level was higher in late 1962 than it had been

---

[44] If the 1-kilometer differential advance of the Dielerhiele Subdelta 1933-41 is also attributed to sedimentation, the rate of true accretion would amount to 125m/yr. However, the Erdete Branch was still quite active at this time, judging by the development of several new bifurcations, although the Dielerhiele began to outpace the Erdete Branch shortly after 1933.

[45] This also finds some support in crude visual estimates of the degree of submergence of Ft. Wilkinson, on the Todenyang shore, between August, 1959 (photographs by F. C. Howell) and August, 1968.

[46] The partial photography of February, 1957, shows that Lake Nagum was a little larger than in February, 1959. This expansion, restricted to the swampy, northern shores, is reflected in the outlines given by Fig. 2-2.

[47] The fort was built shortly after the "pacification" of northern Turkana (1926) to halt the incursions of Ethiopian tribesmen. Deliberately built on a spit, for defensive purposes, the neck of land as well as the foundations were under water in 1968. The fort had already been replaced by a new one on the W1 ridge at Todenyang in May, 1961, but evidence as to its construction is vague and testimony varies: 1931 seems the latest possible date.

Fig. 3-5. The ruins of Fort Wilkinson, partially submerged, in July, 1968.

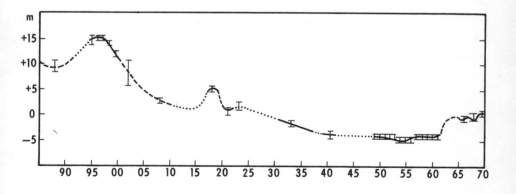

Fig. 3-6. Fluctuations of Lake Rudolf since 1888. Ranges of possible error are indicated by brackets.

for some 30 years. The lake gauge at Ferguson's Gulf was also submerged in 1962 (M. J. Mann, personal communication), placing the level at least 65 centimeters higher than the seasonal high of late 1950. A new gauge was only installed in early 1966, at which time the trend was negative (see Fig. 1-14), so that a temporary high had probably been reached some years before. This is supported by the Gemini IV photography of June, 1965, which shows that submergence in the delta was substantially the same as in 1967-68. Late in 1967 the lake began to rise again, and the level of 1968-70 appears to be identical to that of the late 1920's.

The overall effect of the 1962-65 transgression has been to submerge almost 400 square kilometers of the Delta Fringe, with the lake shore advancing northward an average distance of 12 kilometers. There is no significant change in coastline between the U.S. Air Force photos of December, 1967, and R. I. M. Campbell's of June, 1970.

Application of the Historical Data

Lake Level Fluctuations 1888-1970. The preceding section compiled and attempted a gross evaluation of the changing levels of Lake Rudolf. This information can now by synthesized as in Table 3-1 and Fig. 3-6.

The table (3-1) gives the upper and lower limits for each lake level that can be determined up to 1918, and thereafter states the probable limits of error. High and low-water conditions are indicated whenever the reference dates are precise; seasonal variations were subsequently adjusted by adding 50 centimeters to low-water values, subtracting the same amount from high-water elevations. Finally, the annual values so obtained are averaged within the range of possible error or uncertainty.

Further, qualitative or semi-quantitative data can be added to the graphic representation by adjusting the trends before and after fixed reference points, and by distinguishing continuous, interrupted and dotted segments to indicate degree of reliability. It must be assumed that the inferred, dotted sectors of the lake level curve were complicated by minor oscillations.

The basic outline is that of a falling lake level shortly before 1888, a rise to a +15-meter maximum in 1896, followed by a precipitous drop of 13 meters by 1908. Apart from a violent, positive oscillation of at least 3 meters ca. 1918, the level continued to drop gradually until 1954-56, when the lake was about 5 meters lower than at present. A rapid rise of some 4 meters, beginning early in 1962, brought the lake to about its modern level within 3 years. Contemporary trends are still impossible to verify but appear to be positive.

TABLE 3-1

LAKE RUDOLF LEVELS SINCE 1888

Year	Unadjusted Level (h.w.-August to January) (l.w.-February to July)		Seasonally Adjusted Level	Generalized Annual Level
POSITIVE LEVELS				
1888	8-10m	(l.w.)	8.5-10.5m	+9.5m
1895	13-15	(l.w.)	13.5-15.5	+14.5
1896	15-16	(h.w.)	14.5-15.5	+15.0
1897	14-15	(l.w.)	14.5-15.5	+15.0
1898	14-15	(h.w.)	13.5-14.5	+14.0
1899-1900	12-12.5	(h.w.)'	11.5-12.0	+11.5
1902	5-10	(l.w.)	5.5-10.5	+8.0
1908	2-2.5	(l.w.)	2.5-3.0	+2.5
1918	4-5	(l.w.)	4.5-5.5	+5.0
1921	0-1.5		0-1.5	+1.0
ca. 1923	1-2.5		1.0-2.5	?
NEGATIVE LEVELS				
1933	1.5-2.5	(l.w.)	1.0-2.0	-1.5
1940-41	2.5-4.0	(h.w.)	3.0-4.5	-3.5
1949-53	3.5-4.5	(average)	3.5-4.5	-4.0
1954-56	4.0-5.0	(average)	4.0-5.0	-4.5
1957-61	3.5-4.5	(average)	3.5-4.5	-4.0
1966	0.0-1.0	(average)	0.0-1.0	-0.5
POSITIVE LEVELS				
1968	(±)0.5	(average)	(±)0.5	0
1970	0.0-1.0	(average)	0.0-1.0	+0.5

The Omo Subdeltas after and before 1888. In order to place the 10 major subdeltas of Omo delta plain into a correct temporal perspective, the historical evidence since 1888 can be reviewed:

(a) None of the high Omo stands can be directly linked with the A-subdeltas, and the Omo mouth is invariably indicated at or just upstream of Narok, or somewhere along the uppermost Murdizi Branch. Although remodelling of the A-subdeltas must have taken place during the last century, these features predate 1888.

(b) The B1 and B2 subdeltas were only exposed between the late 1930's and 1961, during which interval the Murdizi Branch was defunct. There is no evidence that deltaic sedimentation occurred in the B1-B2 subdeltas at any time since well before 1888.

(c) The B3 and B4 subdeltas are problematical. In 1933 they were functional, but progradation of subdeltas C1 and C2 had just begun. Consequently the basic morphology of B3 and B4 had been established by 1930. However, the highest parts of the B2 and B3 subdeltas are at or slightly higher than 2 meters above the present lake and would still have been under water in 1919. This leaves less than 15 years for their development. Comparison with subdeltas C1 and C2 and an estimation of progradation rates, discussed further below, shows that B3 and B4 could not possibly have formed in 15 years. Their sedimentation must have begun well prior to 1888.

(d) The evolution of subdeltas C1 and C2 is clearly documented from their incipient stages in 1933 to their partial drowning since 1962. The Erdete Subdelta (C1) appears to have been the major distributary mouth from 1930-40, the Dielerhiele Subdelta (C2) since 1940. The major features visible on the 1959 aerial photography had taken a little less than 30 years to form. However, sedimentation was complemented by a fairly continuous regression of lake level totalling over 4 meters.

To complement the previous synopsis and evaluation, the time required to develop the different Omo subdeltas can be estimated, using various rates of sedimentation. It is, of course, unreasonable to suppose that a single rate of sediment accumulation would apply to each subdelta. Such rates will vary primarily according to changes of sediment flux in the Omo River, and positive or negative oscillations of lake level. It is, furthermore, next to impossible to provide a realistic estimate of the sediment mass in each subdelta, or to ascertain whether one or more discrete periods of accumulation were involved. Nonetheless, a crude attempt will be made to determine the minimum time represented by the formation of the individual subdeltas. In Table 3-2 the length of the central axis of each subdelta is indicated, compensating for multiple distributaries by adding 50% of the length of each major branch in excess of mean delta width. Five different rates of total progradation, grouping the impacts of a lake recession or rise and of sedimentation, are applied.

Perusing Table 3-2, an objective deduction can be made from the case of subdeltas C1 and C2, namely that the maximum rate of total progradation applies if the lake level is actively falling. Yet even under such conditions, subdeltas B3 and B4, together, would have required at least 50 years to develop. Similarly, B1 and B2, together, required at the very least 65 years to evolve, while the A-subdeltas--as a group--span a time interval of no less than 85 years.

Applying these strictures to the field evidence, subdeltas C1 and C2 are, in every sense, contemporary and functional features. Subdeltas B3 and B4, on the other hand, are probably polygenetic and their origins must go back to before the high lake stand of the 1870's that preceded Höhnel's visit. In other words, Höhnel saw the submerged levee woodland of an Omo channel terminating in Subdelta B3. However, development or remodelling of B3 and B4 probably resumed and proceeded before 1930. The Murdizi subdeltas, B1 and B2, clearly are relict features and must have developed during a low-lake phase at least several decades before the mid-19th century. Finally, none of the A-group of subdeltas could have developed in the decade prior to 1899, nor during the relatively

TABLE 3-2

POTENTIAL PROGRADATION RATES FOR THE OMO SUBDELTAS

Subdelta	Adjusted Length of Axis (km)	Possible Rates of Total Progradation				
		100m/yr	200m/yr	300m/yr	400m/yr	500m/yr
A1	9	90 yr	45 yr	30 yr	23 yr	18 yr
A2	14	140	70	47	35	28
A3	13	130	65	43	33	26
A4	7	70	35	23	18	14
B1	20	200	100	67	50	40
B2	22	220	110	73	55	44
B3	19	190	95	63	48	38
B4	14	140	70	47	35	28
C1	16	160	80	53	40	32
C2	11	110	55	37	28	22

high stands of the 1870's or early 1880's. Consequently, the A-group must, as the sub-dued forms suggest, predate the beginnings of Subdelta B3 and even those of B2. Possibly we are dealing with features dating to the 17th or 18th centuries.

Age of the Beach Ridges. An equally conservative evaluation of the beach ridges is warranted. At no time during the last century has the lake level passed the 15-meter shoreline, so that the 20- to 35-meter features predate the mid-19th century. In fact, the preceding discussion of the subdeltas and their evolution suggests that the 20- to 35-meter coastal features can be no younger than the 14th century (see below).

Which beach ridges can be attributed to lake stands since the 1870's? Each of the ridges mapped and identified on Fig. 2-21, and discussed above, once consisted of at least 1 or 2 meters of deposit, spread over a cross-section of 500 meters or more. None could have been built up in a decade, and 30 to 50 years seems a fair minimum estimate for the smaller of these beach ridges. This implies that the lake levels since 1888 can have achieved no more than superficial reworking of the ridges, e.g. of the W4a/E3 shoreline ca. 1895-98 and for a few years before 1880, of the W3b/E2b shorelines ca. 1888, of the W2/E1 shorelines ca. 1907-16 as well as in the mid-1920's, and of the W3a/E2a shoreline ca. 1918-19. If there is any true beach ridge that formed during the past decades, it must now be submerged at about 4 meters below the modern lake surface.

In short, the total of primary beach ridges in the Omo delta plain is "prehistoric" and predates the mid-19th century. However, reworking by younger wave action is to be assumed for forms as high as +15 meters, and eolian processes will have been quite tangible. Theoretically, radiocarbon dating could and should be applied to mollusca from these beach ridges. Unfortunately, however, shell is remarkably scarce and several attempts to obtain suitable materials from the body of these beach sediments failed. In addition, the repeated reworking of surficial deposits by younger, minor transgressions would render dating of the rare surface shells rather questionable.

The Meander Belts before and after 1888. The available information on the state of the river channels since 1888 can be outlined as follows:

(a) The earliest detailed record, the Léontieff map of 1899, shows that the Murle and Shungura Meander Belts have remained substantially unchanged over the past 70 years. The present cut-offs had already been detached, so that the reduction of sinuosity indicated by Stage 4 must have taken place several decades prior to 1899, i.e. when Lake Rudolf was low during the mid-19th century.

(b) The first detailed record of the Narok Meander Belt, the aerial photography of 1940-41, is too young to be relevant to the argument, but the cut-offs in this sector must be of comparable age to those further north. Despite temporary submergence ca. 1880 and again 1890-1900, meander geometry cannot have changed significantly.

(c) The highest levee silts of the central and lower Murdizi River emerged from the lake waters about 1908, at which time their longitudinal profile had already been warped by differential subsidence. Similarly, the Murdizi subdeltas emerged "ready-made" during the late 1930's. In other words, the central and lower segments of the Murdizi channel have been relict since well before 1888. The alternate channels of the upper Murdizi assigned to stages 2 and 3a are substantially older still.

This perspective indicates that Stage 4 of the meander belt development was initiated by the middle of the 19th century. By corollary, the maximum sinuosity of Stage 3a must be associated with one or more of the protracted, high lake levels of the 17th or 18th centuries.

Geomorphologic Conclusions

An Appraisal of Delta Evolution since 1888. During the past 70 to 80 years the course of the Omo River has remained remarkably stable. Yet the lake has fluctuated repeatedly in a range of 20 meters, between 15 meters above and 5 meters below the present level. The consequences have been considerable in terms of physical submergence or emergence, and have presumably had repercussions on vegetation and human settlement. But the geomorphologic impact has been limited:

(a) The changes of lake level have been too brief to provoke a significant change in meander belt geometry or gradient, despite a 30- to 40-year rise of base level prior to

1898 and a 60-year lowering of base level since 1899. This does not preclude minor changes in channel width and depth which, nonetheless, cannot be quantified with the available data.

(b) Fluctuation was so rapid, with superimposed oscillations, that wave-action was unable to sculpture any lasting beach forms, except for minor ridges such as those currently forming on the "high" wave-energy shores of Lake Rudolf (see chapter 2).

(c) There is no evidence to link these repeated ups and downs of the lake with shifting distributary channels or subdeltas, and the major Omo discharge has followed the modern river course to the Erdete-Dielerhiele bifurcation since the mid-19th century except, of course, during periods of submergence. Specifically, for over a century, the Erdete and Dielerhiele have served as the principal or sole mouths of the Omo whenever the lake level has been below +2 or 3 meters.

(d) The protracted drop of lake level 1930-60 did, however, accelerate the progradation of Subdeltas C1 and C2 and, to a lesser extent, of Subdeltas B3 and B4. Beyond these foci of alluviation, it is to be expected that sediment covers deposited during the past 70 or 80 years are almost negligibly thin.

A Hypothesis of Delta Evolution before 1888. The most interesting changes in the Omo Delta predate 1888. These events can now be synthesized, in relative terms, and tentatively interpreted on the basis of time-estimates derived from observed changes since 1888. To allow an overview of these changes through time the available data is outlined, beginning with the youngest events:

(i) Some years before Höhnel's visit Rudolf had been a little higher than in 1888, probably at +10 to +15 meters. This transgression submerged the Omo River from the B3 Subdelta to the Narok bifurcation and had killed but not eradicated the former levee woodland--vestiges of which were still evident in 1897. Allowing a minimum of a decade to kill off the forest, the lake must have been high throughout the 1870's.

(ii) Subdelta B3 and the related Omo levee woodland developed over a period of at least 30 and possibly as much as 50 years, at a time the lake level was between -1 and +3 meters. Allowing at least a decade for the 10- to 15-meter rise in level before 1870, Höhnel's levee woodland and Subdelta B3 formed during a 30- to 50-year time interval prior to 1860. The last of the Stage 3b cut-offs must date from this time.

(iii) Subdeltas B1 and B2, and the related Murdizi (Stage 3b) Branch developed over no less than 65 years in relation to a lake at least 1 meter below present level, and more probably at -3 to -5 meters. Allowing a minimum age for phase (ii), B1 and B2 would span the years 1765-1830, although both the duration and age may be somewhat greater. The initiation of the channel-straightening recorded by Stage 3b would thus fall into the 18th century.

TABLE 3-3

GEOMORPHOLOGIC EVOLUTION OF THE OMO DELTA PLAIN
DURING LATE HOLOCENE TIMES

Lake Level	Beach Ridges	Meander Belts	Subdeltas	Estimated Time "Short" Chronology	"Long" Chronology
0 to -5m	Submerged	Stage 4	C1, C2	1933-1970	
-1.5 to +2	(W2, E1)*	Stage 4	(B3) B4	1920-1933	
+8 to +15	(W3b, E2b)	Stage 4	(A1-A4)	1870-1902	1860-1902
-1 to +3	W2a, E1	Stage 3b/4	B3, ?B4	1830-1860	1800-1850
-3 to -5	Submerged	Stage 3b	B1, B2	1765-1830	1695-1800
+8 to +15	1, 3b, 4a;E2b, 3	Stage 3a	A1 to A4	1680-1765	1545-1695
±0 to +8	W2, 3;E1, 2a	Stage 2		1530-1680	1345-1545
±0 to +10	W2, 3;E1, 2	Stage 1		?1350-1530	?1150-1345
Below +25	W4;E3, 4	Stage 0		?	?
+25 to +35	W5, 6, 7;E4, 5	Murle Lake Plain		?	?

*Parentheses indicate remodelling.

(iv) Subdeltas A1 to A4 and Stage 3a were related to a long period of high lake levels, fluctuating at between +8 and +15 meters. Conservatively, this time interval must be assessed at 85 years or more; 100 to 150 years are more likely. Depending on the variables, Subdelta A1 began to form at some time between the mid-16th and the late 17th century. Many or most of the shoreline features at +10 to 15 meters evolved during this period.

(v) Stage 2 of the meander belts marks a long and complex period of increasing channel sinuosity that must have rivalled or exceeded either Stage 3 (some 150 to 200 years) or Stage 4 (at least 120 years) in duration. Allowing a span of 150 or 200 years, Stage 2 would have been initiated at some time between the 14th and 16th centuries. Lake Rudolf was no higher than +8 meters for any appreciable length of time; instead, it would appear that the level was initially at or a little below that of the present, gradually rising.

(vi) Stage 1 of the meander belts relates to a lake level no higher than +8 or 10 meters, and probably somewhat lower. A minimum time span of several centuries is again indicated.

(vii) Finally, there is the Murle Lake Plain. This rather massive formation must span at least a millennium, at which time Lake Rudolf fluctuated at +20 to +35 meters. Dissection of the emerging lake beds may have begun as early as the 12th or as late as the 14th century.

In other words, the geomorphology of the meander belts and of the "functional" delta plain has a time depth of 600 to 800 years. This data is summarized in Table 3-3.

CHAPTER 4

SHORELINE CHANGES AND DELTA LAND USE

> . . . at the time of Teleki . . .
> a great part of this corner of
> the lake was dry, and . . .
> what was cultivated land in
> those days is now under water,
> thus restricting the area of
> moist ground suitable for
> growing crops.
>
> --Arthur Neumann, 1898

Introduction

The environmental changes implied by the lake fluctuations of the last several centuries are substantial. Shorelines shifted in response to the changes of lake level while the discharge of the Omo River must have waxed and waned as well. Between 1898 and 1955 the delta shoreline moved about 60 kilometers, exposing over 800 square kilometers of fresh land in the delta alone. On the other hand, about 200 square kilometers were inundated between 1888 and 1895, and again some 350 square kilometers between 1962 and 1965. In the meanwhile, Sanderson's Gulf has alternately been a bay of Lake Rudolf and a mudflat with a playa of changing dimensions. Surely these changes cannot have been inconsequential to the inhabitants of the delta.

It is difficult, however, to assess the impact of these environmental factors in the Omo Delta. For one, there are a large number of relatively small tribes living and interacting within the general area. The subsistence and settlement patterns of these tribes vary in detail and are adjusted to the available resources in ways that are not properly understood. The ethnographic literature is woefully inadequate and at times contradictory. And, finally, there have been other, incisive external events since 1888 that had considerable impact on the delta populations. Consequently it is not possible to point to a few simple conclusions about the economic and social effects of environmental change.

The present chapter first attempts to give a summary statement of the delta inhabitants and their immediate neighbors. With this basic information, the available travellers' accounts are evaluated to search for possible repercussions of the shoreline changes of Lake Rudolf. A more definitive study of the ecological implications of the various transgressions and regressions is in preparation by C. J. Carr.

Tribes of the Delta

The lower Omo Basin is occupied by a number of tribal groups, the approximate distribution of which is shown by Fig. 4-1. This tentative map of present tribal lands is based on (a) the best available ethnographic overview of the Omo lowlands, that of Pauli (1950), (b) information obtained by the writer, by C. J. Carr, and by other members of the Chicago Expedition, and (c) complemented for the eastern highlands and Stefanie area by Jensen (1959: map 2).[1] The extensive blank areas appear to be largely unutilized at this time. According to the traditional linguistic classification, the people of the lower Omo Basin fall into three groups: (a) Nilo-Hamitic tribes, such as the Turkana and Bume, (b) Hamitic (Cushitic) tribes, including the Dasanech, Arbore and Borana, and (c) tribes of Nilotic affinities, speaking a number of apparently isolated languages and including the Mursi, Kerre, Murle, Amarr, Batchada, and Banna (Tucker and Bryan, 1956).[2]

The largest delta tribal group, the Dasanech, occupy the Delta Fringe and Flats, the Narok Meander Belt, and the adjacent Beach Ridge Plains and littorals. Officially known as Geleba in Ethiopia and as Marille in Kenya,[3] the Dasanech speak an independent language, apparently related to the Hamitic (Cushitic) languages of the Arbore and Konso (Bryan and Tucker, 1956: 130), northwest and northeast of Lake Stefanie. It appears that the Dasanech originally lived south or west of Lake Rudolf, from where they may have been expelled by the Turkana, possibly at the beginning of the 19th century (Höhnel, 1890: 38f.; Stigand, 1910: 223; Pauli, 1950: 160, 169). Very little is known of their social organization, but a social anthropological study was initiated by Uri Almagor (The Hebrew University) in 1969.

At present the Dasanech are to a large extent semi-sedentary, living primarily in villages or village-clusters that vary in size from a few huts to large agglomerations of several hundred.[4] Huts are of the beehive type, constructed of branches or saplings,

---

[1] The maps of language distribution in the lower Omo Basin given by Cerulli (1956) and Tucker and Bryan (1956) are grossly inaccurate.

[2] Tribal designations and variable orthography pose a problem. Simply for the sake of consistency, the system of Pauli (1950) is adopted here (with the German form tsch rendered in English as ch) for the sake of convenience. Competent linguists must ultimately resolve the problems of orthography, including those of place names.

[3] The terms Reshiat (Höhnel, 1894; Smith, 1897) and Rusia (Cavendish, 1898) apparently refer to the Dasanech name for the northern end of Lake Rudolf, which is Rus according to both Bulatovitch (1900) and Léontieff (1900). Alternate renditions of Geleba include Gheleba, Gelubba, Gellaba, Gelleb and Gallop; synonyms for Marille include Merille and Marle, although the last applies more correctly to a tribe north of Lake Stefanie. Unfortunately the ethnographic synthesis of the Dasanech by Cerulli (1956: 81ff.) erroneously considered the Geleba and Marille as distinct tribes.

[4] No reliable population data is available, although Tucker and Bryan (1956: 131) quote an unpublished estimate of 2,160 adult males, presumably from before the Italian interlude in Ethiopia.

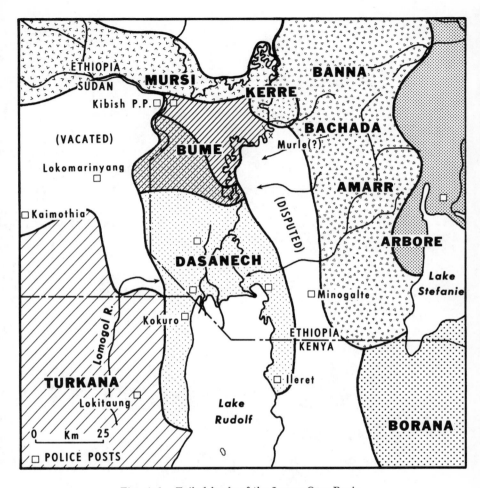

Fig. 4-1. Tribal lands of the Lower Omo Basin

bound together by fibers and covered with hides or grass matting. They are often associated with circular or elliptical stock-pens of thorn fencing, or with swarms of granaries that consist of thatched, beehive structures resting on a small platform. Some villages are enclosed by fences. Several of these settlement types are illustrated by Figs. 4-2 to 4-5. The approximate distribution of Dasanech (and Bume) villages in the delta is shown in Fig. 4-6, based upon helicopter surveys in 1967 and 1968, complemented for the meander tracts and the northeast Rudolf littoral by the air photos of December, 1967. This map is necessarily incomplete and, in the areas of major settlement concentration, somewhat generalized. It does, however, give a general picture of the distinctive localizations of settlement apparent in 1967-68.

Fig. 4-2. Irregular Dasanech settlement cluster, southwest of Kaalam. Note the three small stock pens for juvenile animals. July 1968 (K. W. B.).

Fig. 4-3. The defensive village of Lokibanya northeast of Lake Rudolf is surrounded by 3 concentric rings of thorn fence. According to Atiko Akiru the men and boys sleep in the intermediate ring, while the women and children sleep in the 100 or so huts of the core. August 1967 (K. W. B.).

Fig. 4-4. The rectangular plan and gabled houses of the Kaalam Police Post contrast strongly with the morphology of the Dasanech villages. August 1968 (K. W. B.).

Fig. 4-5. The Dasanech village of Narok, with separate clusters of huts (in clearing at right) and granaries (at left). The Omo levee forest is sharply demarcated from the silt berm, once used more extensively for agriculture and now possibly in fallow. The dugout canoes are primarily used for fishing. July 1968 (K. W. B.).

136

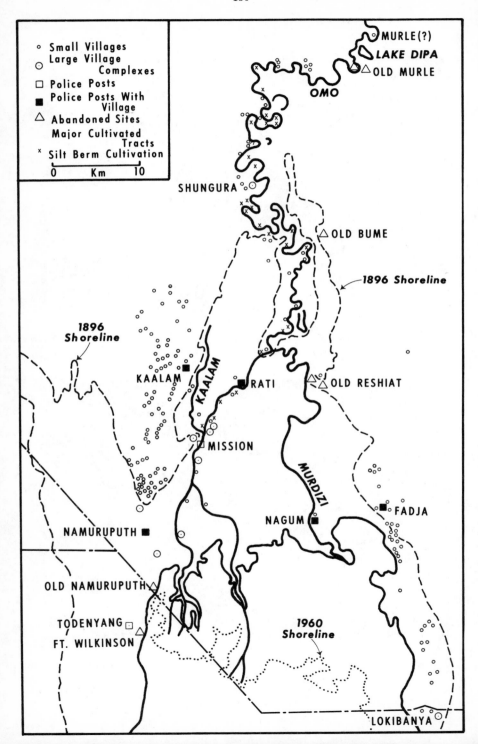

Fig. 4.2. Settlement Locations in the Omo Delta (1967-1968)

The economy of the Dasanech is based primarily--but in a highly variable degree--
on stock-raising, agriculture and fishing (C. J. Carr and J. R. Swart, pers. comm.).
The principal crop is millet (sorghum), together with maize, beans, several gourds and
tobacco. Cultivation is limited to widely dispersed and rather small fields on the silt
berms of the Narok Meander Belt, and farther downstream along the Omo towards the
Kaalam Mission, in a few swales on the bed of the Murdizi and Kaalam Rivers, and on low,
flat surfaces just beyond the levees, particularly among abandoned distributary channels
both southeast of the Kaalam Mission and again east of the Erdete Branch (Fig. 4-6).
Each of these areas is seasonally flooded by the Omo or inundated by seepage waters (see
chapter 2). Practically no irrigation is used in this primitive form of flood basin agriculture, although simple ditches may occasionally be dug to trap the flood waters (J. R. Swart,
pers. comm.). Millet and other crops are sown as the annual flood waters recede, and
sufficient moisture is held in the more clayey soils to bring a single crop to maturity. The
rains (see Fig. 1-9) are too unreliable and usually too limited to be of more than local or
occasional value for dry-farming. In general, only a very small segment of the delta environment can be utilized for this type of cultivation. Stock-raising centers around zebu-
type cattle, goats, sheep, a few camels and, especially to the northeast of Lake Rudolf,
some large herds of donkeys. The complex patterns of grazing have been studied by
C. J. Carr. For the present discussion it can be noted that cattle are largely precluded
from the riverine zone upstream of Rati, on account of tsetse, while recent political measures have excluded the Dasanech from their traditional grazing lands in the southeastern
Sudan (see Nalder, 1937: 148). In fact, the arbitrary political confines have disrupted
established patterns of transhumance, restricting the Dasanech in greater degree to a
semi-sedentary subsistence around their home base but without changing the rather broad
spectrum of mobility.

The second tribal group of the delta, the Bume (also Puma, Donyiro and, more
correctly, Nyangatom), are found along the Shungura and Murle Meander Belts upstream
to Lake Dipa. However, the Bume extend northwestwards to the lower Kibish valley and
formerly reached some 150 kilometers into the Sudan, from the Donyiro Mountains to the
Moru Agippi Plateau. The Bume, who may number about 5500 (Tucker and Bryan, 1956:
110), speak a Nilo-Hamitic dialect derived from Toposa and closely related to Turkana.
In fact, according to Toposa tradition, the Donyiro split off at the beginning of the 19th
century and moved eastwards from the Toposa homelands in the southernmost Sudan
(Nalder, 1937: 65).

The Bume along the Omo settle in tight clusters of large dome-shaped huts, often
set among circular granaries, with conical thatched roofs (Fig. 4-7). Crops similar to
those of the Dasanech are planted on the alluvial flats, but no cattle are kept here. The
complex seasonal patterns of Bume subsistence between the Omo Delta and the Kibish
River will be discussed by C. J. Carr.

138

Fig. 4-7. Bume settlement north of Shungura, with huts set among swarms of
granaries. July 1968 (Elisabeth Butzer).

The last delta group, the Murle (also Marle or Murrile), is problematical. A
tribe of this name was encountered by a number of travellers between 1888 (Höhnel, 1890:
38; 1894: 203f.) and 1903 (Brooke, 1905), and the village formed a landmark on most maps
(see Figs. 3-2 to 3-4), presumably on account of the ford at this locality. Léontieff (1900)
describes the village as hidden amid the riverine forest, Smith (1897: 302f.) specifies 3 villages, each with 200 huts, while Bourg de Bozas (1902) noted villages on both river banks,
surrounded by strong palisades of branches. The various authors agreed that the Murle
cultivated millet and maize, raised goats, sheep and donkeys--but no cattle (Smith, 1897:
303), hunted elephant and fished with complex nets. Stigand (1910: 231) found the east bank
site had disappeared and saw no people at all, but presumed the Murle lived on the other
side of the river. Helicopter survey in 1967 and 1969 showed no traces of villages or
other evidence of settlement on either bank at the Murle site, although there is a cluster
of isolated riverine settlement just upstream of Lake Dipa.[5]

---

[5]The linguistic affinities of the Murle remain uncertain since Höhnel (1894: 203)
claimed the Murle spoke Donyiro, Bulatovitch (1900) noted similarities with both Donyiro
and Didinga, Brooke (1905) with Karimojong, while Cavendish (1898) thought the language
to be different from that of neighboring tribes. Unpublished notes by Bòttego suggest close
Didinga ties, but Pauli (1950: 149f.) has given reason to believe that this information per-
tains to the Murle visited by Bòttego in the Sobat Basin.

Delta Land Use in 1888

The Omo Delta was occupied by the Dasanech (Reschiat) at the time of Höhnel's and Teleki's visit in 1888 (Höhnel, 1890: 38ff.; 1894: 160ff.). According to Höhnel, these people were primarily engaged in the cultivation of millet (dhurra) and the raising of large herds of zebu cattle, goats, sheep and donkeys for milk or meat. They kept dogs but no fowl. In addition they grew two types of beans and a little, poor-quality tobacco. Coffee and additional tobacco were purchased via other tribes upstream while iron objects were obtained from the Amarr. The major village of those Dasanech east of the Omo River was situated on the Nargi Beach Ridge (see Figs. 2-2 and 4-1) and had between 100 and 150 huts. Economic activities were focused on seasonal cultivation in the river flood basins and on herding upon the alluvial fans to the east.

The Dasanech were divided by the river into two sections, with their own heads, and Höhnel was not allowed to visit the Dasanech west of the river. On the basis of information that there were 4 large villages west of the Omo and 3 to the east, Höhnel ventured to estimate the total delta population at about 2000 to 3000. He considered the physical type to be Nilotic, more negroid than the other Hamitic tribes to the east of Lake Rudolf. Women of the Samburu (Maasai) and Rendile (Somali) tribes were sought in marriage, and Höhnel was informed that 3 small Samburu and Rendile settlements were interspersed among the western Dasanech (Höhnel, 1894: 138ff.; 1938). The fishing folk in Alia Bay also were Dasanech. Numbering some 150 or 200 people they kept a few sheep, dogs, and 2 cows, but imported millet from the delta Dasanech in return for help with the harvest.

The Dasanech were friendly, dignified and did not engage in raiding; they appeared to be hostile to both the Turkana and Samburu.[6]

In addition to obtaining direct or indirect information on several of the neighboring tribes, Höhnel (1890: 37f.; 1894: 202ff.) visited the southernmost Bume settlement briefly. This was a village of 30 or 40 huts, ringed by palisades of tree branches and situated on the east bank of the Omo River. Millet was the major crop, together with beans, gourds and tobacco. There were no cattle, suggesting that tsetse may already then have been prevalent in the riverine woodlands. The ubiquitous granaries along the way were mistaken for guardhouses.

The Transgression of 1888-1897

In the years immediately following Höhnel's visit, Lake Rudolf rose some 5 or 6 meters and inundated both the Eastern Flood Basin and the Western Delta Flats (see chapter 3). The possible significance of this transgression can only be gleaned from a limited

[6]The Samburu or Burkeneji found east of Lake Rudolf by Höhnel (1894: 170f.) were displaced by the Borana during the 1890's (see Haberland, 1963: 151).

number of incidental references.

The lake was actually rising in 1888, rather early in the season, since in mid-May of that year Höhnel (1894: 200f.; 1938) was witness to a relocation of the Dasanech village next to his camp. The old site, located near the lower slope of the Nargi Beach Ridge, was apparently in danger of being severed from its grazing lands. In a little more than a week a new village had been constructed on or near the crest of the ridge.

This site did not change appreciably between 1888 and 1895-1896, when Smith (1897: 295f.), Neumann (1898: 289) and Bòttego (Vannutelli and Citerni, 1899: chap. 13) found the eastern Dasanech clustered around the same stie on the Nargi Beach Ridge. Smith estimated the eastern Dasanech at about 500 and states that many had moved to the north-western shore of the lake. Vannutelli and Citerni (1899: pl. IV) schematically show 4 villages scattered along the eastern beach ridges over a stretch of 12 kilometers, north from the Nargi Ridge. These lie well north of the modern settlements found east of the Murdizi today, but in part are still within the fringes of Dasanech grazing territory.

Smith (1897: 295f.) in mid-summer of 1895 and Cavendish (1898) in the late spring of 1897 found the eastern Dasanech "starving, " but attributed this to the loss of all their cattle to the rinderpest (ca. 1891) and of most of their donkeys to repeated Borana raids. In addition, they had been attacked by the Murle.[7] Neumann (1898: 289, 339) may unwittingly have put his finger on two factors of additional importance when he noted the mosquito breeding grounds along the marshy edges of the delta and was told that most of the land cultivable in 1888 was presently under water. The loss of all clayey soils to the lake and the presumed increase of malaria appear to have contributed their share to the sorry state of the eastern Dasanech.

Little specific is reported on the western segments of the tribe at this time, but Vannutelli and Citerni (1899: pl. IV) plot 7 Dasanech (Gheleba) villages[8] on the ridges south of Kaalam, as well as 3 major clusters of their villages west of Sanderson's Gulf, as far south as the Lomogol River. This, in conjunction with Austin's (1899) observations, verified Dasanech settlement west of the Gulf. However, both Smith (1896) and Austin (1899) allude to recent movement into this area. Interestingly, Cavendish (1898) claims that the Dasanech paid an annual tribute to the Turkana in order to be left in peace, although a number of deserted villages west of Sanderson's Gulf were related to recent Turkana raids. Cavendish also mentions a village of fishermen that was built on piles some 300 meters out into the shallow lake waters.

---

[7]Of further interest is that Höhnel (1894: 207) witnessed the beginnings of a smallpox epidemic among the eastern Dasanech.

[8]There also were some Rendile in this area according to Vannutelli and Citerni (1896: 368), as there had been in 1888.

Although it is difficult to isolate other calamities from the pressures imposed on the Dasanech by the submergence of their best agricultural lands, it seems that the years prior to 1897 were ones of great stress.

The Bume had by 1896 occupied several new village sites along the swampy shores of the lake, on low beach ridges east of the Eastern Flood Basin (see Fig. 4-1) (see Neumann, 1898: 294f.; Vannutelli and Citerni, 1899: 329, pl. IV). However, Bòttego's map leaves no doubt that the great mass of Bume settlement was concentrated west of the Omo River and in the Kibish lowlands. The indirect index of precipitation on the Ethiopian Plateau provided by the high level of Lake Rudolf and by the Nile flood volume (see chapter 5 below) suggests that both the Omo and Kibish discharge should have been well above average in the years before 1898. This would imply that cultivation on the Kibish and Omo floodplains was optimal at this time.

The descriptions of Smith (1897: 302f.), Neumann (1898: 304ff.), Vannutelli and Citerni (1899: 362), as well as Cavendish (1898) all agree that the Murle were strong and numerous in 1895-1897. Like the Bume, the Murle may have benefited from high flood levels in the riverine environment--during the very years that the Dasanech lost much of their agricultural lands to the rising waters of Lake Rudolf.

At the end of the 1890's the lower Omo Basin was incorporated into the modern state of Ethiopia, with significant short and long-term results. Four Amhara campaigns[9]

---

[9] The first incursion into the lower Omo Basin was undertaken after the Kingdom of Kafa had been destroyed in September of 1897 (Huntingford, 1955: 105; Athill, 1920). Ras Wolde Giyorgis, who was to be the feudatory lord of Kafa until 1914, established a firm military base at Bonga and in January, 1898, set out to conquer the pagan tribes of the southwest. In the company of A. K. Bulatovitch, he reached Lake Rudolf at a point just west of the Omo River on April 6 and began the return march only 4 days later. Bulatovitch (1900) mentions no clashes other than a minor incident with some Donyiro near Nakwa; no reference is made to the Dasanech.

The second incursion followed the subjugation of the Sidama tribes in southern Ethiopia. At the turn of 1898/99, a major Habte Giyorgis received the voluntary submission of the Borana east and south of Lake Stefanie (Jensen, 1959: 22; also Maud, 1904), but his forces left a trail of terror down the eastern shores of Lake Rudolf into Samburu country (Wellby, 1900: also Stigand, 1910: 224).

The third incursion was decisive for the delta. It was commanded by the Russian colonel Léontieff, with a complement of 8 French officers, a number of Cossacks, 120 Senegalese riflemen, 50 mounted Arab scouts and a half-battery of Maxim machine-guns (Léontieff, 1900). Together with 800 Amhara regulars and their camp-followers, this mobile striking force left Bako for the Usno country, August 11, 1899. Following a skirmish with the Mursi, just below the Usno confluence, Léontieff found the Murle villages abandoned but claims to have ordered his men not to loot the rich granaries found nearby. About August 21, somewhere in the thorn bush east of the Bume village, Léontieff was attacked by as many as 6000 natives--presumably Dasanech and Donyiro. Although the tribesmen were only armed with bows, poisoned arrows and spears, a bloody but unsuccessful battle was fought for almost 4 hours during which 216 Amhara were killed. This seems to have been the sole attempt at organized resistance. Léontieff spent almost 2 months exploring and setting up several permanent police posts in the lower Omo Valley,

in the Omo-Rudolf area can be verified between 1898 and 1903. They succeeded in drawing the Ethiopian frontier west of the delta and from there across the northern end of Lake Rudolf to the southern tip of Lake Stefanie. The immediate impact of this Ethiopian expansion into the tropical lowlands was to depopulate the delta by decimating and expelling the bulk of the inhabitants. For the Dasanech the conquest came after a decade of increased economic hardship, and the destruction and looting of food resources[10] may have had a greater effect on mortality than did the actual warfare. The available reports suggest that the Dasanech, Bume and Murle were much harder hit than their neighbors. These incisive events are quite relevant to the subsequent evaluation of the regression after 1898.

The Impact of the Regression after 1898

Several decades of wet years in East Africa came to an abrupt end by 1899, and between 1897 and 1902 Lake Rudolf dropped about 7 meters, to a level lower than in 1888. By 1908 the lake had fallen a total of 12.5 meters in 11 years, implying a net loss of 9.10^9 cubic meters of water per annum. A sharp decrease of Omo discharge is evident for the years 1899-1900 (see chapter 3), while the failure of even the groundwater supply led to the total abandonment of the Kibish lowlands in 1907-1908 (Gwynn, 1911). At about this time the annual Nile volume at Aswan 1898-1907 averaged 28% lower than that of 1888-1897 (see U.S. Dept. of Commerce, 1959: 1325), and the implications for rainfall trends

---

while his French aide, a major Chedeuvre, marched down the west side of Lake Rudolf, raiding the Turkana as far south as the Kerio River.

The fourth and last great raid came late in 1903. It is referred to by Brooke (1905), and the same war-party penetrated Turkana to well south of the Turkwell River, so that the Turkana requested British assistance (Gulliver and Gulliver, 1953: 54).

[10] Austin (1899) visited the delta some 5 months after the first campaign of April, 1898. He found the Murle country laid waste, the cattle driven off, granaries burned to the ground, young crops destroyed in the fields and the starving population suffering from smallpox. The Dasanech communities west of Sanderson's Gulf had also recently received an influx of refugees fleeing from the Amhara.

The after-effects of Léontieff's war-party were reported at first hand by Smith (1900) and Austin (1902). In December of 1899, Smith found the eastern Dasanech gone and no traces of their villages. West of the river there only were a few groups of huts. It appears that most of the Dasanech, who sustained frightening losses in the battle, fled en masse into Turkana country--to Lokomarinyang, Lokitaung and even Lodwar (Atiko Akiru, pers. comm.)--or took refuge on the marsh islands of the delta fringes (Stigand, 1910: 223f.; Smith, 1900). Murle was found abandoned as late as April, 1900 (Harrison, 1901), but its inhabitants had returned, impoverished and decimated, by April of 1901 (Austin, 1902b: 151f., 169ff.; see also Smith, 1900). The Kerre had vacated the eastern bank of the Omo River (Austin, 1902), while the Mursi seemed to have escaped major ravages (Smith, 1900) but proved hostile and withdrawn (Austin, 1902).

Finally, for 1903, Brooke (1905) noted that the advance guard of the Amhara force had driven off between 30,000 and 40,000 head of stock and taken a great number of slaves. The crops of the Dasanech had been destroyed, so that they were forced to subsist from fish in the delta marsh fringe.

in Ethiopia are unmistakable. In other words, while the delta flats emerged to provide fresh farmlands, the alluvial flats of the Omo, Kaalam and Kibish Rivers presumably shrank in the wake of reduced discharge.

The effects of delta emergence must have been positive for the Dasanech. By 1908 (see Fig. 3-3) the Western and Central Delta Flats, the Eastern Flood Basin, and a good part of both Sanderson's Gulf and the Southern Delta Flats had been re-exposed. This amounted to approximately 280 square kilometers of new land in the immediate delta, and again that much in the Gulf. As the shoreline receded, the Dasanech could have planted their crops on the freshly exposed lake beds. Emergence provided about 560 square kilometers of land in 11 years, or about 50 square kilometers per annum. Even if cultivated for only one season, 5000 hectares (12,350 acres) of cropland would have been enormous and beyond the capacity of the Dasanech to plant and harvest.

The travellers' reports seem to indicate that the Dasanech recovered rapidly after the trepidations of 1899. In 1902 they were sufficiently strong to bring the Kibish Bume into some sort of dependency (Bourg de Bozas, 1903; Hodson, 1929), and Bourg de Bozas (1903) commented on their large herds of sheep, goats, cattle and donkeys. By 1909 the Dasanech had, in large numbers, reoccupied their tribal lands both west and east of the delta (Escherich, 1921: 146ff.; Stigand, 1910: 223ff.).

Although information is totally inadequate, the declining discharge of the Omo presumably reduced the crop potential of the riverine zone among the Omo Bume, Murle, Kerre and other tribes upstream. The Murle were still observed to be starving by Austin (1902b: 169ff.), two years after Léontieff's war-party, while even later Bourg de Bozas (1903: 98) found the Omo Bume emaciated and showing all the symptoms of a severe misère physiologique. Possibly relevant, too, is the last mention of riverine agriculture among the Kerre by Bourg de Bozas (1903); today there are no cultivated tracts between White Sands and a little north of Lake Dipa. The many complications of these and other changes in the riverine zone are illustrated by the diversity of oral tradition from the Narok Meander Belt (see C. J. Carr, in preparation).

Implications of the Transgression of 1962

The rapid, 4-meter rise of Lake Rudolf that began late in 1961 submerged most of the Delta Fringe within 2 or 3 years. Excluding the large bodies of existing open water, over 300 square kilometers were flooded. Most of this was marshy terrain in the interdistributary basins, but extensive tracts of dry ground were lost adjacent to the Erdete and Dielerhiele Branches, particularly on the levee backslopes.

The ecological impacts of this recent transgression have been studied in detail by C. J. Carr and will be published in due course. On the basis of her work it can be concluded that the resulting loss of grazing and crop land, possibly with the increased expanse and proximity of mosquito breeding habitats, forced the evacuation of most of the Dasanech in the Delta Fringe to areas west of the Omo River. The lower Erdete and Dielerhiele had evidently been major centers of population and cultivation and their loss imposed considerable hardships and subsequently increased grazing pressures on the western Beach Ridge Plain (Carr, pers. comm.).

CHAPTER 5

LAKE RUDOLF AND EAST AFRICAN CLIMATE

> The large-scale circulation of
> the atmosphere during the cur-
> rent decade has produced pat-
> terns that had never been seen
> earlier in this century, but
> which seem to represent a
> recurrence of a regime that pre-
> vailed over long periods before
> 1895. . . . It is an urgent prac-
> tical matter to take stock of the
> present climatic position and to
> assess the probability of the new
> climatic regime continuing . . .
>
> --Hubert Lamb, 1966

Introduction

It remains to evaluate the fluctuations of Lake Rudolf in a climatological context.
The levels of closed lakes can be expected to reflect the climate of their drainage basins,
but the interrelationships of the several variables involved are complex. Stated in theory,
influx from runoff + direct precipitation on the lake = evaporation from the lake surface, if
we can assume that subterranean water loss by deep seepage is negligible. None of
these variables is readily measured, even under optimal circumstances, and in the case
of Lake Rudolf they cannot even be estimated with a reasonable degree of accuracy. In
addition, the Omo-Rudolf basin extends longitudinally across several climatic provinces,
so that the factors governing influx from runoff cannot be expected to co-vary uniformly in
either direction or amplitude. The station network of the Omo-Rudolf basin is minimal,
and the available records are quite brief. Finally, the lake levels themselves as reconstructed from 1888 to 1941 and as gauged intermittently from 1949 to the present provide
only an approximate and discontinuous record. Consequently it is not only impossible to
develop a realistic equilibrium model for the hydrology of Lake Rudolf but it is also not
yet possible to apply rigorous tests to compare lake fluctuations with other variables.

Allowing that a fully objective interpretation of the fluctuations of Lake Rudolf will
be precluded for at least several more decades, an examination of the qualitative data is

nonetheless pertinent. The levels of this lake have fluctuated over a range of 20 meters within the past 75 years, an amplitude exceeding that of any other world lake of natural origin. The difference represents a volume of 15×10^{10} cubic meters or about a meter of water across the entire drainage basin. To what extent can these changes of the hydrological balance be rationalized, and how do they compare with those reflected by other East African lakes, by river discharge, and by other related phenomena? These questions are the theme of this concluding discussion.

The raw data employed in this chapter are derived from a variety of sources. Station data from Ethiopia were supplied by the National Climatological Service of Ethiopia, with the Addis Ababa record prior to 1960 available in the World Weather Records (U. S. Dept. of Commerce, 1959: 151f.; 1967: 152); station data from Kenya and the gauge readings for Lake Victoria (since 1961) were provided by the East African Meteorological Department. Lake level data for Naivasha were provided by the Water Development Division, Nairobi, while the gauge readings for Lake Victoria and Nile discharge at Aswan (to 1954) are available in the World Weather Records (U. S. Dept. of Commerce, 1959: 1325ff.; 1967: 521); Nile discharge values 1955-1969 were provided by the Nile Control General Inspectorate of the Egyptian Ministry of Irrigation. Finally, the Sobat as well as Bahr al-Jebel discharge until 1957 is published by Hurst and Phillips (1935: 184ff.; 1939: 90f., 98f.), Hurst and Black (1963: 90f., 106f., 110f.), and the Nile Control Staff (1965: 106f.), with data for 1958-70 supplied by the Sudanese and Egyptian Ministries of Irrigation.

Variations of Rainfall and Temperature over the Omo-Rudolf Basin

Several climatic variables can be examined within the Omo-Rudolf basin: (a) rainfall over the upper and middle Omo Basin, (b) direct rainfall on the lake, and (c) evaporation from the lake surface.

Rainfall over the Ethiopian Plateau. The better records of the upper Omo Basin begin in 1953-54, and the most complete of these is Wush Wush (see Table 1-3). Occasional missing months are readily interpolated from nearby Bonga,[1] and the record can be smoothed by 3-year running means to provide the curve shown in Fig. 5-1. The initial rise of Lake Rudolf in 1961 (see Fig. 1-14) was paralleled by a slight increase of rainfall at Wush Wush which reached a maximum for the triad 1961-63. After a low in 1964-66, a

---

[1]The response time of Lake Rudolf to seasonal fluctuations is about 3 months, i. e. the time lag between maximum Omo discharge and maximum lake level. Response to secular variations of hydrological equilibrium has not been determined but is probably on the order of 3 to at most 5 years, judging by the application of 3 and 5-year running means to series of climatic or discharge values applied in this chapter.

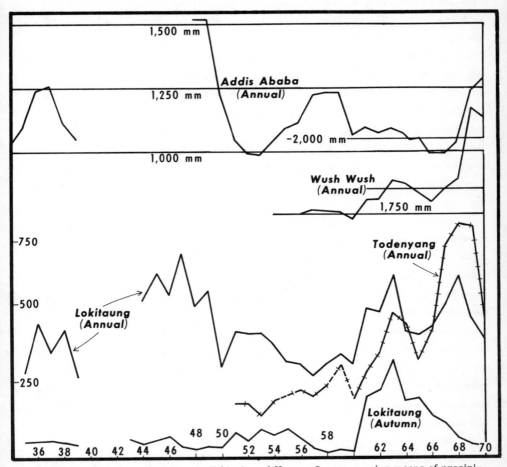

Fig. 5-1. Select Stations in Ethiopia and Kenya: 3-year running means of precipitation.

new and striking maximum was attained in 1967-69. For the brief period of comparison, the overall directions of change correspond well with the changes in level of Lake Rudolf, but the amplitudes are quite out of proportion. Examination of the monthly rainfall totals at Wush Wush for the key years 1961 to 1963 show only 3 unusual months that received in excess of 200% the monthly average: November and December, 1961, and May 1962. The same applies to the wet years of the late 1960's, where November 1967, December 1968, and October 1969 each received in excess of 200% their average totals. It does not appear, therefore, that the summer rainy season was significantly intensified but rather that the rainy season was prolonged. In particular, the spring or autumnal submaxima are accentuated and extended to span most of the winter months. So, for example, rainfall at Wush Wush was consistently well above average from August through December of 1961, from January through July of 1963, and again from December 1968 through March 1969.

The only long sequence from the Ethiopian Plateau is that of Addis Ababa (1902-39, 1946-70). Employing 3-year overlapping means, the annual rainfall shows maxima in 1915-17, 1928-30, 1946-48 and 1968-70, minima in 1918-20, 1931-33, 1951-53 and 1965-67 (see Fig. 5-1 for part of this curve). These fluctuations bear no resemblance to those of Lake Rudolf since 1902 or to precipitation at Wush Wush since 1954. Rainfall at Addis Ababa also shows no obvious similarities to the variable flow of the Nile or Sobat Rivers (see below). Evidently short-term climatic trends across the Ethiopian Plateau are far from uniform.

Direct Rainfall on Lake Rudolf. It has been established that Lake Victoria receives appreciably more rainfall than its immediate shores, and the rainfall maximum near the center of the lake receives 2300 millimeters compared with 1000-1500 millimeters on the adjacent coastal sectors. This anomaly is attributed to regular nocturnal land breezes above the lake which lead to a marked frequency peak of nocturnal and early morning convergence and thundershowers (Flohn and Fraedrich, 1966). Rudolf is far more narrow than Victoria and the available information does not seem to support the notion of a land breeze (see chapter 1). However, the discrepancy of 308 millimeters rainfall at Ileret on the east shore and of 380 millimeters at Todenyang on the west shore--at comparable latitudes--indicates that the lake does, at least slightly, influence precipitation patterns. The possibility remains that convection cells and precipitation activity over Lake Rudolf are accentuated during periods of disturbed weather.[2]

In order to test this hypothesis the rainfall records of Lokitaung and Ileret were examined. Although too incomplete to show graphically, the Ileret record is interesting: the highest yearly total since 1957 was 680 millimeters--in 1961--and the highest monthly total 263 millimeters, in November of 1961. Rainfall at Ileret was also above average in 1963, 1967 and 1968. The Todenyang curve can be shown by 3-year overlapping means if 1955 and 1959 are interpolated from Lokitaung, as in Fig. 5-1. Except for the very dry year 1965, rainfall 1961-1970 has been appreciably higher than 1949-1960. The unusually high triads ending in 1967, 1968 and 1969 reflect on an aberrant rainfall total of 299 millimeters for July of 1967. Although not a coastal station, Lokitaung provides the longest available record (1933-39, 1942-1970) within reasonable proximity of Lake Rudolf. The

---

[2] Either rain "areas, " i.e. large-scale rainfall systems that develop and persist over periods of days (see Johnson, 1962), or linear "cloud lines" of a more mobile type (see Hammer, 1971).

seasonal components were examined individually and show interesting differences. The summer rains (July plus August) exhibit no secular trend, but the autumn rains (November plus December) do. The latter are represented in Fig. 5-1 by 3-year overlapping means that emphasize unusually heavy autumn rains from 1961 to 1965. These autumn rains are responsible for the total precipitation peak for the triad 1961-63, during which years the spring rains (March, April and May) were normal. Other precipitation peaks in the 1930's, in 1945-47 and 1966-68 reflect almost exclusively on spring rains.

The visual similarities of rainfall trends at Lokitaung and Todenyang with fluctuations of lake level are considerable for the last 20 years, although obscure prior to 1949. However, it is not possible to make a conclusive case for a really substantial increase of rainfall directly over the lake.

Evaporation from the Surface of Lake Rudolf. Lacking direct measurements of evaporation or systematic data on windspeed, any attempt to consider changes of evaporation is strongly circumscribed. Temperature remains the one variable of relevance, and the only series in lake proximity is that of Lodwar (1947-1970, with interruptions in the minimum readings 1949-50). Examination of the Lodwar record and its seasonal components showed no trends of even superficial similarity to the ups and downs of Lake Rudolf. Fig. 5-2 depicts the trends of mean daily maximum and minimum temperatures, both annually and for summer (July plus August), smoothed by 3-year running means. Lower maximum temperatures can best be explained by increased cloud cover, particularly when accompanied by higher minimum temperatures. Such may have been the case 1954-66. The unusually cold minima of the late 60's are difficult to explain since they were most pronounced during both the summer and winter months. In no case can it be argued that temperatures were exceptionally low or cloudiness possibly greater during the crucial years 1961-63.

Recent History of Lake Stefanie

The fluctuations of Lake Rudolf since 1888 find a close counterpart in the history of Lake Stefanie (see the review of Zavattari, 1942). This promises to shed further light on the mechanisms controlling Lake Rudolf, so that a brief discussion is warranted here.

Stefanie has alternated between a shallow lake and a salt pan since its discovery by Teleki and Höhnel. The floor is estimated to lie at about 520 meters (Merla, 1963; Mohr, 1964) and its area can be estimated at 1200 square kilometers on the basis of the 1:250,000 map (Series Y 503, sheet NB-37-13). The drainage basin has an area of approximately 21,000 square kilometers, and the maximum watershed elevation is close to 4000 meters. The major influx is obtained from that part of the basin between 5 and 6° N latitude and

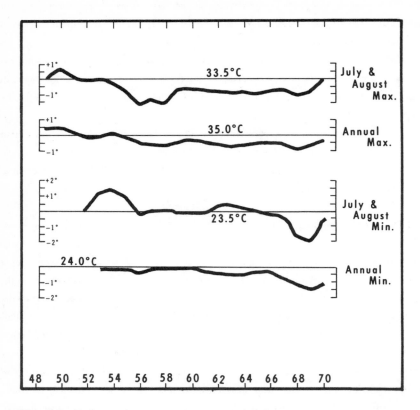

Fig. 5-2. Lodwar: 3-year running means of daily maximum and minimum temperatures.

36^0 40' and 38^0 E longitude. One of the two major tributaries, the Galana Dulei, has a basin comparable in most ways to that of the Usno River (see Fig. 1-13 for hydrographic patterns). The other, the Galana Sagan, drains the Ethiopian Rift south of Lake Chamo. These rivers combine as the sole perennial affluents entering Lake Stefanie from the north, across a broad, deltaic lowland. As such the Stefanie Basin is a replica of the lower Omo Basin (including the Usno drainage, but excluding the complications introduced by a long deep lake, by the drainage of the Uganda escarpment and, above all, by the middle and upper Omo Basins. If indeed Rudolf and Stefanie have behaved identically, the responsible short-term climatic changes should presumably be sought along the southern and western peripheries of the Ethiopian Plateau.

In late April of 1888, Höhnel (1894: 186ff.) found Stefanie to be a saline lake with many fish and crocodiles. Although his guide claimed that the southern shoreline had receded several hundred meters in the preceding 3 years, no salt precipitates were visible

around the perimeter. In June of 1895, Smith (1897: 248f.) found the northern shores
marshy and soundings showed that the lake was flat-bottomed although at least 7.5 meters
deep, with fish, crocodiles and hippos abundant. The dry lake flats noted by Höhnel at the
southern end of the lake were now submerged and grown over with vegetation as much as
2 meters tall. Comparable observations were made at the northern end of the lake by
Bòttego (Vannutelli and Citerni, 1899: 339ff.) in September, 1896, and Cavendish (1898) in
March, 1897. It would appear that Lake Stefanie was mildly regressive in 1888 but transgressive in 1895-97, at which time the entire lake floor (as shown on the modern 1:250,000
map) was under water (see the 1:1 million folding map of Vannutelli and Citerni, 1899).

In December 1899 (Smith, 1900) the southern end of Stefanie was dry and covered
with dead fish while Harrison (1901: 258) found the lake bone dry in March, 1900, its surface "strewn with shells and heaps of fishbones." This condition was confirmed by later
visitors in 1901, 1903, 1908, 1922 and 1938-39 (see Zavattari, 1942), who variously
described the floor as dry mud or dry swamp, at times with an ephemeral playa lake of
restricted dimensions and no more than 2 meters deep. It appears that Stefanie remained
a playa until the early 1960's, since the 1961 maps of Series Y503 and Y633--based on air
photos of 1959--show no more than marsh. However, the peripheral Gemini photo of June,
1965 (S-65-34796) suggests dry lake flats but with dark vegetation apparent along the southern shoreline. In the course of reconnaissance with the Piper Cherokee in July, 1968, the
writer found the whole basin filled and the shoreline similar to that mapped by Bòttego.
There were extensive, marshy flats along the northern end of the lake (Fig. 5-3), while
the waters encroached directly on the piedmont alluvial plain along the western shore.
However, tall shoreline vegetation and salt precipitates at 1 or 2 meters above the watermark, both along the western shore and some of the volcanic islands in the southeastern
part of the lake, indicate that Stefanie had been higher and deeper very recently, presumably in 1967. Several generations of water influx were suggested by algal concentrations
along horizontal discontinuities, separating waters of variable turbidity, and, presumably,
salinity.[3] This dramatic transformation into a true lake probably paralleled the rise of
Lake Rudolf after 1961. In between, from 1898 to about 1961, Lake Stefanie was essentially dry at a time that Lake Rudolf dropped from +15 to -5 meters. Lake Stefanie is,
then, subject to the same basic climatic controls as Lake Rudolf. In January, 1970,
Grove and Goudie (1971) found the lake essentially dry once again and make no mention of
the shoreline vegetation conspicuous in 1968. However a thin sheet of salty and turbid
water developed in the wake of rains on the lake flats. This suggests that the lake is now
once more deteriorating into a salt pan.

---

[3]It probably is relevant that the waters off the western shore are relatively clear
whereas there are several kilometers of highly turbid water along the eastern coastal
perimeter.

Fig. 5-3. The northern part of Lake Stefanie, looking east across the marshy
Galana Sagan Delta. Note the algal line foreground. July 1968 (K. W. B.).

Other East African Lakes

The trends of Lakes Rudolf and Stefanie do not stand isolated. Lake Victoria and
lakes of the Eastern and Western Rifts also declined at the end of the 19th century, with
high levels the rule since the early 1960's. The behavior of these other East African
lakes is pertinent for a climatological interpretation of the vicissitudes of Lake Rudolf.

Gauge readings are available for Lake Victoria since 1899 (see Fig. 5-4). The
lake fluctuated within a fairly restricted range until 1961, the highest peaks coming in
1906 and 1917-18, the lowest level in 1922. Between late 1961 and early 1964 the lake
rose rapidly by 2. 2 meters and has fluctuated at a relatively high level since. Lamb (1966)
summarizes earlier observations that about 1878-79 the lake was higher than in 1964, that
the level fell during the 1880's, and that it recovered somewhat to an intermediate level
about 1892-95. The parallelism with Lakes Rudolf and Stefanie requires no emphasis.
Mörth (1967) studied the climatic parameters controlling the hydrological equilibrium of
Lake Victoria; for the years 1938-1964 he found a very high correlation (r = +0. 96) between
monthly rainfall over the Victoria catchment ahd change in lake level from the mean level
of the first 10 days of one month and the mean level of the next following month. This

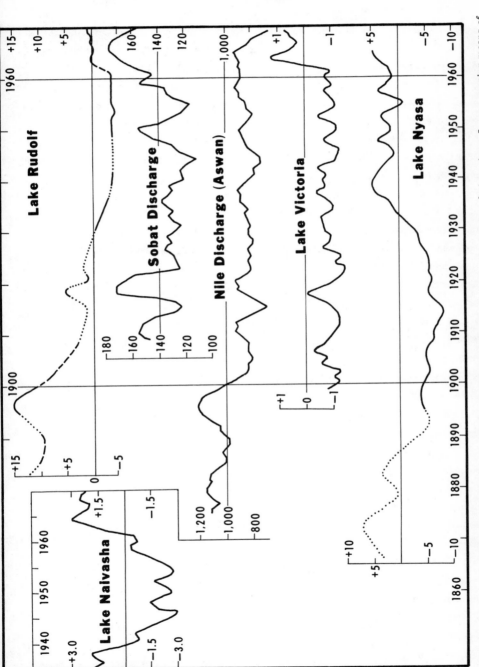

Fig. 5-4. Annual Fluctuations of Lake Levels and River Discharge in East Africa. Levels in meters; 5-year running means of discharge in 10^8 cubic meters; note scales vary. Broken lines inferred.

predictable and very rapid response is due to the fact that 85% of the lake water is lost by evaporation (Lamb, 1966)[4] and that a high proportion of the water is derived from direct precipitation over the lake (see Flohn and Fraedrich, 1966).[5] In other words, the ups and downs of Lake Victoria over the last century have been a direct response to secular trends of the equinoctial rains over the Victoria catchment, between latitudes 2° N and 3° S.

Less complete records for the lakes of the Eastern Rift in Kenya and Tanzania suggest low levels during the first half of the 20th century, with marked rises during the early 1960's. The longest series of gauge readings is that of Lake Naivasha (1935-70), which shows a progressive fall from 1938 to 1946 and a rapid rise from 1961 to 1964 (Fig. 5-4).[6] Comparable rises of 2 or 3 meters during the early 1960's have been experienced by Lakes Baringo and Nakuru (M. J. Mann, pers. comm.) as well as Lake Manyara (personal observations, 1968).

The case of Lake Tanganyika ($3-9^o$ S), outlined by Lamb (1966), is complicated by the temporary silt bars that frequently close off the overflow to the Congo River. The lake was low during the first part of the 19th century, but high in 1874 and 1879, at which times there was a strong outflow. Thereafter the lake fell and was low from a little before 1896 to 1960, after which it rose almost 3 meters. Minimum levels were probably reached in the 1920's and again between 1948 and 1956 (Lamb, 1966).

Finally, a long record is also available for Lake Nyasa (Malawi) (Fig. 5-4).[7] There were high stands in the early 1870's and early 1880's, with a generally low level from 1890 to 1930. Since the late 1930's Lake Nyasa has fluctuated around a mean comparable to that of the 1870's. Here the divergences with Lakes Victoria and Tanganyika are appreciable and climate trends no longer uniform, suggesting that the Nyasa Basin ($9-15^o$ S) is outside of the broad East African sphere in which recent climatic anomalies have been largely similar.

In general, it appears that lake levels were relatively high throughout East Africa during the second half of the 19th century. This moister climate came to an end earlier in the south than in the north, e.g. during the 1880's in the Nyasa, Tanganyika and Victoria basins, and in 1898 in the Rudolf and Stefanie basins. After several dry decades, the Nyasa Basin became wetter in the 1930's, at a time when lake levels in the Eastern Rift

---

[4] Only 13-15% flows out over the threshold at Jinja to enter the Nile River.

[5] The lake has a surface area of about 68,000 sq. km. while that of the total basin is about 196,000 sq. km. (Lamb, 1966).

[6] Compensating for a change of datum in 1936. There may, however, have been another such change about 1958.

[7] After Pike (1965) but incorporating the correction factor communicated by the East African Meteorological Department to Lamb (1966).

were falling conspicuously. Then, in 1961, lake levels from Tanganyika in the southwest to Rudolf and Stefanie in the northwest began to rise rapidly.

No meteorological explanations have yet been advanced to explain the anomalies of the 1960's, despite their many economic implications across the width of East Africa. However, Mörth (1971) has shown the progression of the abnormal rains of late 1961 across East Africa by means of monthly charts, and both Lamb (1966) and Mörth (1971) have marshalled a wealth of precipitation data that leaves no doubt that rising lake levels during the early 60's were directly linked to increased rainfall and, in part, accompanied by major floods. The major deviations may have been concentrated at low and inter-mediate elevations, below 1800 meters (Lamb, 1966); however, there also appears to have been an increase in precipitation above 3400 meters on Mt. Ruwenzori, where several small glaciers between late 1961 and mid-1962 interrupted a spectacular overall retreat (underway since 1958) and where only the highest mountain streams increased their flow markedly between late 1961 and mid-1963 (Temple, 1968).

The Sobat and Nile Rivers

The last class of comparative evidence from East Africa is provided by stream discharge in the Nile system. Most pertinent here is the Sobat River which drains the western peripheries of the Ethiopian Plateau between latitudes 6 and 9° N via its principal tributaries, the Baro, Akobo and Pibor. In fact, the Sobat drains the highlands and foot-hills immediately west of the Omo and Kibish basins. It should be expected, therefore, that the Sobat and Omo discharge have experienced similar trends. Sobat volumes have been measured near the mouth of the river, a little upstream of Malakal, since 1905. Unfortunately this record was interrupted from September, 1964, through December, 1965, by the revolts in the southern Sudan, although the data can be extrapolated from other gauge readings. By applying 5-year running means the fluctuations of annual volume from 1905 to 1963 are rendered in Fig. 5-4. They show peak flows in the pentads 1906-10, 1915-19, 1946-50 and 1961-65. Minimum flows occurred 1911-15, 1922-26, 1940-44 and 1951-55. Comparing this with the levels of Lake Rudolf, the 1918-19 peaks coincide exactly, and the preceding and subsequent lows are compatible. The complex increase of discharge during the late 1950's climaxed in 1966 and is broadly compatible with the rise of Lake Rudolf, possibly with a greater time lag. However, the discharge peak 1946-50 that is closely paralleled by rainfall statistics from Lodwar to Addis Ababa finds no reper-cussions in Lake Rudolf and is equally insignificant on the Bahr el-Jebel discharge curve from Mongalla--as reflecting Nile drainage south of 5° N latitude.

It is noteworthy that Sobat summer discharge has fluctuated but little since 1905; instead the major anomalies reflect on major deviations of winter and spring discharge.

So, for example, in the case of the discharge peaks 1917-18 and 1962-63 the major anomalies were volumes in excess of 200% the normal during January and February 1917, January through May 1918, January through March of 1962 and 1966-67, and again January and February of 1963 and 1965. This supports the conclusion that the rainy season was greatly prolonged in 1917, 1918, 1962-63 and 1965-67, with a secondary autumn maximum. This suggests that anomalies on the Ethiopian Plateau reflect on rainfall during the transitional seasons far more than they do on the nature of the summer monsoon sensu strictu.

A much longer record is provided by the combined Nile waters that pass through Aswan. Volume of flow has been measured here since 1871 and the record is unquestionably homogeneous (see Hurst and Phillips, 1935; also Lamb, 1966), at least until the inauguration of the High Dam in 1964. The 5-year running means shown by Fig. 5-4 are broadly parallel to the shorter Sobat curve, except for the absence of a peak in 1959-63. The general correspondence is reasonable since 80% of the Nile waters are derived from the Blue Nile, Atbara and Sobat Rivers; the discrepancy in 1959-63 may well indicate that these years were not unusually wet in central and northern Ethiopia, and this indeed is implied by the Addis Ababa records. At a gross scale the high discharge before 1900 and the radically reduced flow thereafter document closely the abrupt discontinuity of rainfall inferred for most of East Africa on the basis of the lake levels. Even in detail the high Rudolf levels prior to 1888 and during the mid-1890's find close counterparts in the Nile volume. After 1900 the more muted fluctuations of discharge find a partial but by no means satisfactory correspondence with the levels of Lake Rudolf.

In the context of the preceding discussions of other variables, the discharge curves of the Sobat and Nile show significant divergences as well as striking similarities with the trends of Lake Rudolf. Considering that we are dealing with unlike phenomena from external although adjacent areas, the parallelisms are good in terms of long-term trends. It is therefore reasonable to expect that the old records of Nile floods from A.D. 622 through the 19th century (Jarvis, 1936)[8] should find many basic parallels in the Omo-Rudolf basin. These floods were relatively high from the 620's to the 750's, from the 1090's to the 1190's, from the 1380's to the 1450's, during the early 1500's and around 1600, from the 1720's to the 1770's and, finally, from the 1840's to the 1890's.[9] Floods were relatively low from the 750's to the 1080's, from the 1190's to the 1380's, from the 1450's to the early 1500's, during the late 1600's and early 1700's, and from the 1770's to the 1840's. A direct correlation of these trends with the levels of Lake Rudolf inferred for the six to eight centuries

---

[8]As gauged by the Roda Nilometer at Cairo. The records are rather incomplete from 1523 to 1689.

[9]When annual maxima are smoothed by 10 or 20-year running means and compensating for the progressive but not uniform rise of the river bed.

prior to the 1880's (Table 3-3) is precluded by a lack of firm dating in the Rudolf case. It is tempting, however, to compare the +8 to +15-meter Rudolf level of Stage 4 with the high Nile floods from the 1840's to the 1890's, the preceding low levels from -5 to +3 meters (Stage 3b) with the low Nile floods from the 1770's to the 1840's.

Comparisons with Mid-Latitude Lakes

Before concluding, it is of interest to examine the trends of higher latitude lakes in North America and Asia for the past 100 years or so. These records provide a broader, planetary perspective as well as some notable contrasts. Good data is available from Lake Michigan since 1860 (see U. S. Dept. of Commerce, 1965: 500f; data 1961-70 supplied by U. S. Army Corps of Army Engineers), Great Salt Lake since 1851 (data supplied by the U. S. Geological Survey, Water Resources Division; see also Greer, 1971), the Caspian Sea 1837-1962 (Bagrov, 1963) and the Dead Sea since the 1830's (Klein, 1961; data 1961-70 supplied by the Israel Hydrological Service). The curves, as presented in Fig. 5-5, are all distorted by increased diversion of water and other human interference.[10]

Bearing these negative trends in mind, the superimposed fluctuations can be seen to share some similarities among themselves but none with those of the East African lakes. No uniform trends can be identified for the late 19th century, but hydrological budgets were generally positive from about 1905 to 1930, negative during the early 1960's. In fact, the Dead Sea seems to fluctuate inversely with respect to the East African lakes, being unusually high from 1895 to 1955.[11]

Climatic Conclusions

The preceding chapter has amply shown that it is unrealistic to speak of climatic "stability" in East Africa. Beyond this hard fact a number of general deductions can be made:

---

[10]The waters of Lake Michigan have been increasingly intensively used for domestic and industrial purposes since the late 19th century, while the Volga waters that provide most of the Caspian influx have been diverted by hydroelectric projects, industrial and domestic consumption, as well as irrigation since the 1930's. The major affluents of Great Salt Lake have been tapped for irrigation and drinking water on an increasingly large scale since the 1870's. The upper Jordan drainage has been partly diverted for irrigation since the 1930's and particularly since the 1950's.

[11]The careful and unique documentation of the Dead Sea levels through the 19th century by Cippora Klein is complemented by a fine historical-geomorphological study of the Jordan Valley by Schattner (1962). The fact that the Jordan debouches into a non-outlet lake, the Dead Sea, by an incipient delta makes Schattner's study of considerable historical interest. It appears that meander shifts in the case of the Jordan were a little more rapid than in the case of the Omo.

158

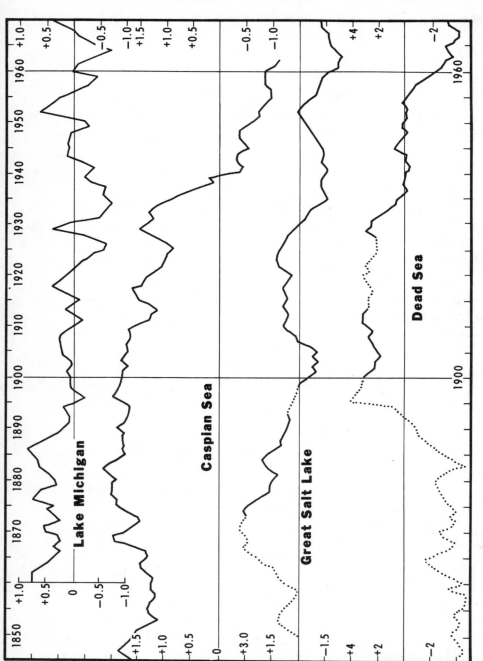

Fig. 5-5. Annual Fluctuations of Lake Levels in North America and Asia. Levels in meters; scales vary. Broken lines inferred. Lake Michigan catchment 42–46° N; Caspian Sea 36–60° N; Great Salt Lake 39–43° N; Dead Sea 30–34° N

(a) Lake Rudolf has fluctuated conspicuously since the 1880's. These changes of level or lake volume show a satisfactory overall correspondence with the levels of Lakes Stefanie, Victoria, Tanganyika, Naivasha and other closed lakes of the Eastern Rift. There also are broad similarities with discharge fluctuations of the Ethiopian Nile catchment in general and the Sobat drainage in particular. Such homologues indicate that climatic anomalies on an intermediate scale, i.e. second-order climatic variations with a duration of several decades, are comparable over Ethiopia and the remainder of East Africa (to latitude 8^0 S).

(b) In detail, the short-term, first-order fluctuations with a wave length of less than 10 years are localized in occurrence and can seldom be recognized throughout East Africa. The only exception to this would seem to be rise of lake levels and precipitation totals during the early 1960's; however, there is reason to believe that this is but the beginning of a longer trend that may persist for several decades. This precipitation increase of the 1960's may be restricted to the belt of equinoctial rains, remaining almost imperceptible in the summer monsoon over Ethiopia.

(c) The perspective of scale seems important in evaluating and comparing trends and deviations in East African climate as elsewhere. To modify a principle attributed to Knut Faegri, the greater the amplitude and wave length of a climatic anomaly, the greater the area affected.

(d) Climatic anomalies involve a number of interacting variables ranging from the general circulation and its dynamic components to more measurable parameters such as radiation, temperature, humidity, evaporation and precipitation. The hydrological equilibria reflected by lake levels and stream discharge are no less multivariate. This accounts for the difficulties in correlating lake levels with stream discharge, or with select climatic parameters over a heterogeneous drainage basin.

(e) Although rigorously proven only in the case of Lake Victoria, the sum total of the East African evidence indicates that changes in lake level or stream discharge over the past several decades have been overwhelmingly if not exclusively a function of precipitation changes. This presumably includes some changes in intensity and seasonal distribution or concentration. But there is as yet no support for significant changes of temperature or evaporation of immediate relevance. This suggests that other first and second-order variations in the past have also reflected primarily on changes of precipitation. The same may well be true of third and fourth-order variations, with wave lengths of several decades and centuries respectively.

(f) Despite the lack of positive correlation with hydrologic equilibria in higher latitudes, the changes of rainfall patterns apparent in East Africa during the late 19th century and again during the 1960's are not idiosyncratic in terms of the general circulation of the atmosphere. Instead they can be related to changes of the general wind circulation and of planetary temperature trends in at least certain latitudinal zones and tropospheric levels (Lamb, 1966; Rudloff, 1967: 151ff., 167ff., 221ff.). Writing of the 1960's, Lamb (1966: 210) is able to observe that:

> In extratropical latitudes since 1960 the zonal character of the circulation has weakened, meridional windstreams have become more important and have penetrated more from high to low latitudes. But near the equator the pattern has become more zonal, at least in the rainy seasons, with a more strongly developed low pressure zone between the diminished subtropical anticyclones, which have been displaced towards lower latitudes.

By way of tentative explanation for the observed changes, Lamb (1966: 211) suggests

> . . . (i) rather generally falling temperatures in the upper troposphere and near the tropopause over the last twenty years or so at latitudes from near 20^0 - 70^0 N, (ii) a decreasing difference between places near the tropic and the polar circle or beyond -- ie. greatest cooling over this period at the high levels over the tropic. Whether this is primarily due to a change in the radiation budget or merely to some change in the internal heat exchange pattern of the atmosphere is not clear; but temperature differences between the equator and the tropic appear to have increased over the same period, and the development of the equatorial low pressure zone seems to have strengthened.

> The present situation, as regards values of indices of the zonal circulation and nature of the wind patterns occurring, apparently resembles the situation before the 'final warming' of the climates in high latitudes from 1895 onwards and abrupt decline of tropical rainfalls about 1890-95. The climatic statistics of times before 1895 may therefore be more relevant to the present day and for some decades ahead than the statistics of any period between 1900 and 1950 (Lamb, 1966: 210).

It is still premature to affirm or negate this prediction, but the economic repercussions will be momentous in either instance.

(g) Finally, there is good reason to believe that the level of Lake Rudolf serves as a useful index of East African climate, in particular of precipitation patterns over periods measured in terms of decades and centuries, and probably also over longer intervals of time (see Butzer, Isaac, et al., n.d.).

APPENDIX A

CLIMATIC OBSERVATIONS BY THE CHICAGO OMO EXPEDITION (1968)

by

C. J. Carr and K. W. Butzer

The absence of comprehensive weather data from the Lower Omo Basin gives value to any series of climatic observations, no matter how brief or incomplete. The most serious gap is in terms of day-to-day weather parameters such as wind speed and directions, cloud cover and type, as well as day-to-day fluctuations of relative humidity. In order to obtain a more dynamic concept of the regional climatology, a wide range of variables was observed during the 1968 season. Wet-and-dry bulb temperatures, wind and clouds were noted fairly faithfully at 7 AM, 2 PM (14 o'clock) and 9 PM (21 o'clock)-- all ±15 minutes. In addition, maximum and minimum temperatures as well as rainfall were recorded. The equipment used consisted of a wet-and-dry bulb thermometer, a max-min thermometer, a simple "fence-post" rain-gauge and a manual anemometer. The thermometers were exposed at 1.5 meters in an open, well-ventilated tent, the hand anemometer held on open ground at 2 meters. Although some inconsistencies undoubtedly occurred in assessment of cloud cover and type, the basic patterns that can be traced from day to day are reliable. Unfortunately the irregular schedules and multiple duties that a field season imposes upon the members of an expedition did not permit an unbroken record. Nevertheless we trust that even the somewhat fragmentary data of Table A-1 will substantially augment our understanding of "weather" in the lower Omo Valley.

TABLE A-1.

CLIMATIC OBSERVATIONS AT CHICAGO CAMP 1968

A. TEMPORARY CAMP, 15 km NE of Lokitaung, ca. 430m elevation

DAY	TEMPERATURES (°C) Max	Min	7	14	21	RAIN (mm)	HUMIDITY (%) 7	14	21	WIND DIRECTION/SPEED (km/hr) Dir 7	Dir 14	Dir 21	Spd 7	Spd 14	Spd 21	CLOUD COVER 7	14	21	TYPE 7	14	21
JUNE																					
11			27	34	29	–	56	36	46	S	SE	S				10	20	60	Ci, Cu	Cu	Ac
12			33	35	28	–	35	37	57	SE	SE	N				70	55	5	Sc	Cu	Ac
13			25	34	28	–	68	46	57	C	E	N				10	5	0	Sc	Sc	–
14			23	32	24	19.1	67	55	83	W	SE	NW	0			85	30	10	Ac, Cu	Ci, Cu	Sc
15			24	36	26	–	83	38	69	C	S	C	3	6	0	60	25	5	Sc	Cs, Cu	–
16			22	32	26	–	74	39	55	S	S	C	8	6	0	75	65	5	Ci, Ac	Cu	–
17			24	32	26	–	68	39	55	SE	SE	N	2	10	3	100	90	0	Cs, Cu	Cs	–
18			24	34	27	–	75	36	50	E	E	NW	5	5	3	0	10	0	Cu	Ci, Cu	–
19			22	35	27	–	74	42	56	SE	S	S	13	24	3	10	50	0	Cu	Cb	–
20			25	36	27	–	61	34	63	SE	S	C	3	5	0	55	10	5	Cs, Ac	Sc, Cu	As
21			25	34	29	–	61	32	46	SE	SE	S	5	19	6	0	25	0	Ci	Cu	–
22			29			–				SE						1			Cs		
Mean	–	–	25.3	34.0	27.0	–	65.6	39.5	57.9	–	–	–	4.9	10.7	2.1	40*	35	10	–	–	–
No. Readings	–	–	12	11	11	–	11	11	11	12	11	11	8	7	7	12	11	11	12	11	11

B. MAIN CAMP, 5 km NW of Shungura, ca. 450m elevation

JUNE																			
23	27	—	—		—	—	—	NW	—	—	5	—	—	0	—	—	-		Cu,As
24	27	38	27		—	75	50	S	S	S	13	8	3	0	25	15	-	Cu	Cu
25	24	33	29		60	35	46	SE	S	SW	1	1	1	25	85	5	Ci,Cu	Cs,Cu	Cu
26	26	33	29		49	35	46	SE	NE	SW	8	6	1	65	85	15	Cu,Sc	Cb,Sc	Cu
27	22	36	28		82	18	45	NE	S	S	3	8	1	65	5	5	Cs	Cs	
28	25	35	29		61	25	40	E	S	S	1	6	13	85	25	0	Ac	Cu	
29	23	35	29		59	29	46	E		C	21	21	0	0	35	15	-	Cu	As
30	25	—	28		47	—	51	S		SW	8	—	1	25	—	15	Sc,Cu	Cu	Sc
Mean	24.9	35.0	28.4	-	59.7	36.2	46.3	-	-	-	7.5	8.3	2.9	35	45	10	-	-	-
No.	8	6	7	-	6	6	7	8	6	7	8	6	7	8	6	6	8	6	5

*Means of cloud cover are rounded off to nearest 5%.

TABLE A-1--Continued

DAY	TEMPERATURES (°C)					RAIN (mm)	HUMIDITY (%)			WIND DIRECTION/SPEED (km/hr)						CLOUD COVER / TYPE					
	Max	Min	7	14	21		7	14	21	7	14	21	7	14	21	7	14	21	7	14	21
JULY																					
1			27.0	38.0	29.0	-	56	54	46	E	S	S	8	16	1	65	35	5	Sc,Cu	Cu	Cu
2			24.0	35.5	28.0	-	60	29	39	S	S	C	8	13	0	0	25	5	Cs	Cu,Sc	Cu,Sc
3	38.0	20.0	23.0	35.0	28.0	-	75	25	45	S	SE	S	5	14	6	5	35	85	Ci	Cs,Cu	Ac
4	39.0		23.0	36.0	28.0	-	59	26	45	SE	SE	S	3	8	1	35	35	0	Cs,As	Sc,Cs	Cu
5	39.0	20.0	25.0	35.0	29.0	-	61	29	46	SE	E	SE	5	10	3	8	15	5	Ci,Cs	Cs,Sc	Ci,Cu
6	38.0	18.0	25.0		30.0	-	61		31	SE		S	5		1	25		75	Ac,Sc	Sc,Cu	Ac,Cu
7	37.0	20.0	26.0		31.0	-	55		43	SE		NE	10		0	85	25	85	Ac,As	Sc,Cu	Sc
8	44.0	19.0	22.0	39.0	27.0	-	82	31	63	SW	NE	S	1	5	6	5	35	55	As	Ac,Sc	Ns,Cs
9	33.0	21.0	24.0	27.0	27.0	8.0	83	70	77	N	NW	C	1	3	0	100	100	75	Ns	Cs,Sc	Cs,Sc
10	37.0	20.0	23.0	37.0		-	91	31		NW	S	C	1	5	0	95	35	8	Ac,Ns	Ac,Sc	Ac
11	36.5	21.5	24.0	34.5	29.0	-	60	33	46	S	E	SE	3	16	8	0	40	20	Sc	Ac,Cu	Cs,Ac
12	38.0	21.5	25.0	35.0	29.0	-	61	27	46	S	SE	S	16	32	1	25	8	0	Cs,Cu	-	Sc
13	37.0	21.5	23.0		27.5	-	71		60	SE		S	10		8	5		5	Sc		Sc,Cu
14	36.5	20.5	23.0	34.0	29.0	tr	71	32	46	SE	S	S	16	19	1	8	35	35	Ac,Sc	Ac,Cu	Ac,Sc
15	38.5	24.0	25.0	34.0	29.5	tr	47	27	43	SE	SE	C	14	10	0	55		5	Ac,As	Ac,Sc	Sc
16	37.5	24.0	25.0		30.0	-	51		39	SE		S	12		5	35		8	Cc,Sc		Sc,Cu
17	38.0	22.0	26.0	37.0	30.0	-	62	27	44	SE	S	C	1	8	0	85	85	15	Ac,Sc	Cs,Cu	Cs,Ac
18	39.0	19.0	25.0	37.0	29.0	-	61	31	52	SE	S	S	16	13	5	15	65	15	Ac,Sc	Cu	Ac
19	39.5	19.0	21.5	37.5	29.0	-	69	24	46	S	SE	S	3	5	1	10	55	10	Cs,Sc	Cu	Cs
20	38.0	21.5	27.0	35.0	27.5	-	47	37	51	E	SE	SE	2	6	3	5	15	0	Cs,Ac	As,Cu	-
21	41.0	23.5	25.0	35.0	27.5	tr			47	E	E	W	8	2	6	45	90	90	Cs,Ac	Fc,Sc	Fs,Cb
22	39.5	21.5	22.5	34.0	31.5	1.4				SE	S	S	2	13	1	85	30	0	Ac,Sc	Cs,Cu	-
23	39.0		24.5	36.0	28.0	-	60	34	45	S	E	SE	12	10	7	1	35	0	As	Cu	-
24		22.5	24.0	36.0		-		34	45		E		6	6		10	35		Sc,Cu	Ac,Cu	-
25	41.5			36.0	29.5	-		34	45		E	SE		6	1		35	0		Ac,Cu	-
26	37.0	23.5	26.0	34.0	29.0	tr	55	36	46	SE	S	S	4	14	2	90	35	0	Ac,Sc	Sc	-
27	37.5	24.0	25.0	37.0	29.0	-		29	37	SE	S	S	8	12	1	25	20	0	Sc,Cu	Cu	-

28	44.0	22.5	25.5	36.5	28.5	–	48	34	52	SE	SE	S	4	6	5	30	35	0	Cs,Ac Ac,Sc	Sc,Cu	–
29	36.5	24.0	25.5	32.0	29.5	–	55	39	49	SE	S	SW	5	8	1	75	95	40	Ac,Sc Sc	Fc Ac,Cu	As,Sc
30	42.5	23.0		38.0	29.0	–		30	49	SE	SE	SE	9	2	1	10	35	5	Sc Ac,Sc	Ac,Cu Cu	As Cs
31	41.5	23.5	25.0	39.0	29.5	–	65	29	47	SE	E	S	1	9	1	25	25	5			–
Mean	38.7	21.6	24.5	35.6	28.8	(9.4)	62.6	33.3	47.4	–	–	–	6.6	10.0	2.5	35	40	20	–	–	–
No.	28	26	29	27	29	(2)	25	24	27	30	27	30	30	27	30	30	27	30	30	27	29

TABLE A-1--Continued

Column groupings are: TEMPERATURES (°C) [Max, Min, 7, 14, 21]; RAIN (mm); HUMIDITY (%) [7, 14, 21]; WIND DIRECTION / SPEED (km/hr) [dir 7/14/21, speed 7/14/21]; CLOUD COVER / TYPE [cover 7/14/21, type 7/14/21].

DAY	Temp Max	Temp Min	Temp 7	Temp 14	Temp 21	RAIN (mm)	Hum 7	Hum 14	Hum 21	WDir 7	WDir 14	WDir 21	WSpd 7	WSpd 14	WSpd 21	Cover 7	Cover 14	Cover 21	Type 7	Type 14	Type 21
AUGUST																					
1	39.0	24.0	26.0	35.0	29.5	-	62	31	46	SE	S	S	8	1	1	45	0	0	Ac	Cu	As
2	40.5	22.5	25.5	37.0	30.0	-	65	35	47	SE	S	SE	6	1	1	15	50	0	As, Ac	Ac	-
3	39.5	24.5	26.5		29.0	-	66		49	SE		S	6		1	100		70	As, Sc		Ac, Sc
4		22.0	25.0		29.5	-	72		41	SE		SE	2		9	98		80	Ac, Sc		Ac
5					29.5	-			41			SE			16			20			Sc
6			25.0		29.5		54			E			15			80			Cb		
7																					
8	39.5	23.0	25.0	38.5	29.5	-	51	40	45	E	SE	SE	12	9	4	35	18	10	Cs, Ac	Cs, Cu	Ac, Sc
9	39.5	23.0	25.0	38.5	28.5	-	58	45	44	SE	S	S	2	11	9	18	10	10	Cs, Ac	Cs, Ac	Cs
10	38.0	21.5	25.0	33.5	28.5	-	63	22	41	SE	S	SE	19	5	9	20	95	5	As, Ac	Cu, Sc	As
11	39.0	23.0	24.5		28.5	-	54		44	S		SE	3		7	0		15	Ac, Sc		Ac, Cu
12	40.5	22.0	23.5	40.0	28.5	-	45	18	50	SE	SE	SE	13	13	4	10	10	25	-	Ac, Cu	Sc
13	44.0	20.0	27.5	44.0	29.0	-	50	21	46	SE	S	S	5	2	5	5	35	0	Ac	Sc, Cb	-
14	41.5	22.0	24.5	41.5	29.5	-	54		41	SE	S	S	17	13	5	10	8	0	As	Cu	-
15	41.5	22.5	24.5	38.5	30.0	-	55	32	56	SE	SE	S	7	5	5	20	25	8	Cc, Ac		Sc
16	42.0	23.5	25.5	38.5	30.0		47	28		S	S	SE	10	8	2	95	45	0	-	Cu	-
17	39.0	23.0	27.0	34.5	30.5	tr	45	33	39	SE	SE	SE	14	8	1	45	25	0	As, Sc	As, Sc	-
18	43.5	24.5	27.5		32.0	-	50		39	SE	S	S	15	2	15	95	40	0	Cc, Ac		-
19	39.5	24.0	26.5	33.0	30.0	-		32	59	N	SE	SE	5		6	95	70	0	As, Ac	Ac, Sc	Ac, Sc
20	39.5	22.5	24.5		29.5	tr	80			SE		SE	8		2	95		75	Fs, Cb		-
21	41.5	23.0	25.0		29.5	-	58		62	S		SE	11		4	0	35	10	-	Cu	As
22	42.0	23.5	25.5	38.0	29.0	-	53	22	55	SE	SE	SE	12	17	14	25	10	0	Ac, Sc	Cu, Sc	Ac
23	40.0	22.0		37.0	29.0	-	71	31	46	S	S	SE	4	9	2	4	25	0	Cs	Cu	-
24	41.5	23.0	26.5	39.0	31.5	-	59	24	41	SE	S	SE	21		2	5		10	Cs	Sc, Cu	-
25	43.0	22.5	23.0		28.0	-	50		67	SE	SE	SE	11	11	5	8	75	10	Ac, Sc	Sc, Cu	Sc
26	38.0	22.5	27.0	35.0	29.5	-		29	62	SE	SE	SE			6	95	75		Ac	Cu	Sc
27	37.5	24.5	26.5	33.5	27.5	-		27	45	SE	SE	S		8	6	85	70		Ac	Ac, Cu	Sc

28	40.0	22.5	24.0	29.0	–	–	57	–	35	SE	S	SE	1	10	0	0	0	–	–	–	–
29	39.5	23.0	28.5	29.0	–	–	64	–	40	SE	–	SE	12	8	25	0	35	0	Cu	Sc, Cu	–
30	39.0	22.0	25.0	37.5	27.5	–	51	31	74	SE	SE	SE	2	19	5	0	0	–	–	Sc	–
31		23.0	28.5			–	47			SE		SE	6			20			Cs		
Mean	40.3	22.8	25.7	37.3	29.3	(0)	57.0	29.5	48.3	–	–	–	9.1	8.4	5.9	40	35	20	–	–	–
No.	26	27	27	17	28	(0)	26	17	26	28	20	27	27	17	27	28	20	25	27	20	28

APPENDIX B

SEDIMENTOLOGICAL ANALYSES

by

K. W. Butzer, C. J. Carr and B. G. Gladfelter

TABLE B-1

SUMMARY DESCRIPTION OF SEDIMENT SAMPLES FROM THE OMO DELTA PLAIN

(From depths of −50cm, unless otherwise indicated. Samples with organic matter shown by asterisks)

Sample No.	Depths (m)	Munsell Color	Stratification	Structure	Texture	Sorting	Oxidation (hue)	pH	%CaCO$_3$	mV
CHANNEL DEPOSITS										
(a) Bed-load facies										
1090	(−0.3)	Dk. gr. brown (10 YR 4.5/2.5)	Moderate	Weak	(Med.-gr) sand	Good		6.9	0.0	+150
(b) Silt bars and embanked silt berms										
965		Brown (10 YR 5/3)	Good	Moderate	Silty clay loam	Moderate		6.8	0.0	+190
1047*		Brown (10 YR 4/3)	Good	Weak	Silty clay loam	Moderate		6.7	0.0	+175
1048*		Brown (10 YR 4/3)	Moderate	Moderate	Silty clay loam	Moderate		7.3	2.2	+185
1049*		Brown (10 YR 4.5/3)	Moderate	Moderate	Silty clay	Moderate		6.9	0.0	+165
1051*		Brown (10 YR 5/3.5)	Moderate	Moderate	Silty clay loam	Moderate		6.9	0.0	+170
1093	(−0.1)	Brown (10 YR 5/3)	Laminated	Moderate	Loam	Moderate		6.6	0.0	+180
1096		Brown (10 YR 5/3)	Good	Moderate	Silty clay loam	Moderate	Some mottling (7.5 YR)	6.2	0.0	+180
1272*+	(−0.05)	Brown (10 YR 4/3)	Moderate	Moderate	Silty clay loam	Moderate		7.4	0.0	+170
1273*+	(−0.2)	Brown (10 YR 5/3)	Moderate	Moderate	Silty clay loam	Moderate		7.0	0.0	+180
1274*+	(−0.6)	Brown (10 YR 4/3)	Moderate	Moderate	Silty clay loam	Moderate		7.0	0.0	+180

(c) Backwater muds and clay plugs

Sample	(Depth)	Color	Structure	Consistency	Texture	Drainage	Mottling	pH		Eh
1050*		Dk. brown (10 YR 4/3)	Massive	Moderate	Silty clay	Moderate		6.6	0.0	--
1092	(-0.1)	Dk. gr. brown (10 YR 4.5/2.5)	Moderate	Weak	Sandy loam	Moderate		6.5	0.0	+170
1095		Brown (10 YR 4.5/3)	Massive	Cracking	Silty clay	Moderate		6.6	0.0	+190

OVERBANK SILTS

(a) Meander Belt

Sample	(Depth)	Color	Structure	Consistency	Texture	Drainage	Mottling	pH		Eh
887		Brown (10 YR 5/3)	Moderate	Moderate	Silt loam	Moderate		6.9	0.0	--
1046	(-1.0)	Brown (10 YR 5/3)	Good	Moderate	Silty clay loam	Moderate		7.4	0.0	+165
1091*		Brown (10 YR 5/3)	Moderate	Weak	Silty clay loam	Moderate	Some mottling (10 YR)	7.4	0.0	+190
1094*		Brown (10 YR 5/3)	Laminated	Moderate	Silty clay loam	Moderate	Some mottling (10 YR)	6.8	0.0	+165
1097*		Brown (10 YR 5/3)	Good	Moderate	Silty clay loam	Moderate	Some mottling (10 YR)	6.9	0.0	+180
1098*		Brown (10 YR 5/3)	Massive	Cracking	Silty clay loam	Moderate	Mottling (7.5 YR)	6.1	0.0	+180
1099*		Brown (10 YR 4/3)	Moderate	Moderate	Silty clay loam	Moderate		7.0	0.0	+180
1303+	(-0.1)	Yell. brown (10 YR 5/4)	Massive	Moderate	Silty clay loam	Moderate	Mottling (10 YR)		0.0	--
1302+	(-2.0)	Brown (10 YR 5/3.5)	Moderate	Moderate	Silt loam	Moderate			0.0	--

(b) Delta Flats

Sample	(Depth)	Color	Structure	Consistency	Texture	Drainage	Mottling	pH		Eh
1052		Brown (10 YR 5/3.5)	Moderate	Moderate	Silty clay loam	Moderate	Some mottling (10 YR)	6.6	0.0	+140
1100		Brown (10 YR 4/3)	Moderate	Weak	Silty clay loam	Moderate		7.1	0.0	+180
1101*	(-0.6)	Brown (10 YR 5/3)	Laminated	Strong	Silty clay	Moderate	Horizontal, ped faces (5-7.5 YR)	6.2	0.0	+185
1102A*	(-1.2)	Brown (10 YR 5/3)	Moderate	Moderate	Silty clay loam	Moderate	Some mottling (7.5 YR)	6.5	0.0	+175

(c) Delta Fringe

Sample	(Depth)	Color	Structure	Consistency	Texture	Drainage	Mottling	pH		Eh
1056*		Dk. gr. brown (10 YR 4/2.5)	Moderate	Moderate	Silty clay	Moderate	Mottling (10 YR)	6.5	0.0	--
1057*		Brown (10 YR 5/3)	Moderate	Moderate	Silty clay	Moderate	Some mottling (10 YR)	6.8	0.0	--
1058*		Pale brown (10 YR 6/3)	Moderate	Moderate	Silty clay loam	Poor	Some mottling (10 YR)	6.8	0.0	--

MUDFLATS AND LAGOONS

(a) Delta Flats

Sample	(Depth)	Color	Structure	Consistency	Texture	Drainage	Mottling	pH		Eh
1044	(-3.6)	Brown (10 YR 5/3.5)	Massive	Moderate	Silty clay	Moderate	Some mottling (7.5 YR)	7.1	0.0	+150

TABLE B-1--Continued

Sample No.	Depths (m)	Munsell Color	Stratification	Structure	Texture	Sorting	Oxidation (hue)	pH	%CaCO₃	mV
1045*	(-2.4)	Brown (10 YR 4.5/3)	Massive	Cracking	Silty clay	Moderate	Some mottling 7.5 YR)	7.9	0.0	+135
1088*		Dk. gr. brown (10 YR 4/2)	Massive	Cracking	Clay	Moderate		6.5	0.0	+200
1089*		Dk. gr. brown (10 YR 4/2, 3/1)	Massive	Cracking	Clay	Moderate	Mottling (7.5 YR)	5.7	0.0	+220
1102B*	(-1.2)	Brown (10 YR 4.5/3)	Moderate	Strong	Clay (salt)	Moderate	FeMn ped faces	6.5	0.0	+170
1103*	(-1.8)	Brown (10 YR 4.5/3)	Moderate	Strong	Clay	Moderate		6.8	0.0	+150
(b) Delta Fringe										
1106*		Brown (10 YR 5/3)	Massive	Cracking	Clay (salt)	Moderate	Some mottling (10 YR)	6.3	0.0	+200
1107*		Brown (10 YR 5/3)	Massive	Cracking	Clay	Moderate	Some mottling (10 YR)	6.1	0.0	
(c) Sanderson's Gulf										
1592*	(-0.2)	Pale brown (10 YR 6/2.5)	Moderate	Moderate	Clay loam	--		8.9	18.2	--
1593	(-0.1)	Brown (7.5 YR 4/2)	Massive	Cracking	Clay	--		9.2	23.4	--
1595+	(-0.6)	Lt. br. gray (10 YR 6/2.5)	Massive	Cracking	Clay	Moderate		8.8	5.6	+140
1597+	(-0.6)	Lt. br. gray (10 YR 6/2.5)	Massive	Cracking	Clay	Moderate		8.8	6.1	+110
1131*	(-0.3)	Dk. gr. brown (10 YR 4/2)	Massive	Cracking	Clay	Moderate		7.5	0.0	+150
FLUVIO-LITTORAL DEPOSITS										
945A*	(-0.3)	Brown (7.5 YR 5/4)	Moderate	Strong	Loam	Poor		7.0	0.0	--
945B	(-1.0)	Pale brown (10 YR 5.5/3)	Moderate	Moderate	Loam	Poor		6.5	0.0	--
1054	(-2.2)	Pale brown (10 YR 6/3)	Moderate	Weak	Med.-sandy loam	Poor		6.7	0.0	+160
1105		Lt. yell. brown (10 YR 6/4)	Moderate	Moderate	Med.-sandy loam	Poor		6.5	0.0	+220
BEACH RIDGES										
944	(-0.2)	V. pale brown (10 YR 8/3)	Moderate	Weak	Coarse sand	Good		7.2	0.0	--
1000*	(-0.3)	Brown (10 YR 5/3)	Moderate	Weak	Loamy medium sand	Moderate		7.9	8.7	+140
1002*	(-0.3)	Pale brown (10 YR 5.5/3)	Moderate	Weak	Coarse sand	Good		8.0	13.7	+180

1006*	(-0.3)	Brown (10 YR 5.5/3)	Moderate	Weak	Coarse sand	Moderate	7.8	14.7	+140
1053		Pale brown (10 YR 6/3)	Moderate	Weak	Coarse sand	Good	6.6	0.0	+130
1055	(-2.6)	Pale brown (10 YR 5.5/3)	Moderate	Weak	Loamy coarse sand	Moderate	6.9	6.3	+165
1104		Pale brown (10 YR 6/3)	Moderate	Weak	V. coarse sand	Good	7.0	0.0	+160
1122	(-0.2)	Pale brown (10 YR 6/3)	Moderate	Weak	Coarse sand	Moderate	8.6	9.7	+150

Abbreviations: dk. (dark), lt. (light), br. (brownish), gr. (grayish), yell. (yellowish), v. (very), and med. (medium-grade).

+ indicates samples collected by C. J. Carr.

TABLE B-2

TEXTURAL DATA (IN PER CENT) FOR NON-CARBONATE

RESIDUES OF SAMPLES CITED IN TABLE B-1

The grade units are:
- (1) Granules   2-6.35 mm
- (2) Very coarse sand   595-2000 microns
- (3) Coarse sand   210-595 microns
- (4) Medium sand   63-210 microns
- (5) Fine sand   20-63 microns
- (6) Coarse silt   6-20 microns
- (7) Fine silt   2-6 microns
- (8) Clay   Under 2 microns

Sample	(1)	(2)	(3)	(4)	(5)	(6)	(7)	(8)
Channel Deposits								
1090	--	0.1	35.5	52.9	7.0	2.0	2.0	0.5
965	--	--	0.1	9.9	36.0	14.0	8.0	32.0
1047	--	--	0.1	11.9	31.5	14.0	10.0	32.5
1048	--	--	0.1	10.9	30.0	14.5	14.5	30.0
1049	--	0.1	0.1	1.3	22.5	22.0	13.5	40.5
1051	--	0.1	0.3	6.1	34.0	22.0	7.0	30.5
1093	--	0.1	0.7	27.7	30.5	12.0	7.0	22.0
1096	--	0.1	0.3	2.1	42.0	16.5	18.0	21.0
1272	--	--	0.1	15.9	31.0	14.0	6.0	33.0
1273	--	--	0.1	12.9	36.0	13.5	6.5	31.0
1274	--	--	0.1	4.9	33.0	20.0	7.0	35.0
1050	--	0.1	0.1	0.8	25.0	24.5	10.0	39.5
1092	--	0.1	0.9	65.5	14.0	7.5	4.0	8.0
1095	--	0.1	0.2	3.2	23.2	15.0	14.5	44.0
Overbank Silts								
887	--	--	0.1	2.9	31.0	27.5	13.0	25.5
1046	--	0.2	0.5	6.8	42.5	13.0	9.0	28.0
1091	--	--	0.1	0.4	33.0	28.0	15.0	22.5
1094	--	0.1	0.1	0.3	25.0	30.5	18.0	26.0
1097	0.1	0.6	0.4	0.9	36.0	26.0	14.0	22.0
1098	--	0.1	0.1	0.8	34.5	24.0	10.0	30.5
1099	--	0.1	0.1	0.3	39.0	24.0	13.0	23.5
1303	--	0.2	0.5	0.8	36.5	22.0	9.0	32.0
1302	--	--	0.1	0.3	44.5	20.0	9.0	26.0
1052	--	0.1	0.1	2.8	35.0	17.5	10.0	34.5
1100	0.1	0.1	0.1	5.2	40.0	15.0	10.0	29.5
1101	--	0.1	0.1	0.3	21.5	28.5	16.0	33.5
1102A	--	0.1	0.1	0.3	26.0	28.0	13.0	32.5
1056	--	--	0.1	8.9	25.0	15.0	9.0	42.0
1057	--	--	0.1	1.4	33.5	17.5	12.5	35.0
1058	--	--	0.1	11.9	29.5	14.5	10.0	34.0

TABLE B-2--<u>Continued</u>

Sample	(1)	(2)	(3)	(4)	(5)	(6)	(7)	(8)
Mudflats and Lagoons								
1044	--	0.1	0.1	0.4	24.5	20.0	14.0	40.5
1045	--	0.1	0.3	2.1	20.0	21.0	11.5	45.5
1088	--	--	0.1	0.9	11.5	17.5	9.0	61.0
1089	--	0.2	0.1	1.2	6.5	10.0	11.5	70.5
1102B	--	0.1	0.1	0.3	12.0	25.0	12.5	50.0
1103A	--	0.1	0.1	0.8	13.0	18.0	20.0	48.0
1103B	--	--	0.1	0.4	11.0	17.0	17.0	54.5
1106	--	--	1.3	6.7	15.5	18.5	9.5	48.5
1107	--	--	0.1	3.9	22.0	15.5	9.0	49.5
1592	--	0.1	2.8	25.1	72.0[t]			
1593	--	--	0.2	6.1	93.7[t]			
1595	--	0.1	1.0	14.5	10.5	15.5	8.5	50.0
1597	--	0.1	0.8	4.6	6.5	15.5	12.5	60.0
1131	--	0.1	0.5	4.4	8.0	13.0	10.0	64.0
Fluvio-Littoral Deposits								
945A	--	2.1	11.7	31.7	17.5	10.0	4.0	23.0
945B	--	3.8	15.5	23.7	17.5	13.0	6.5	20.0
1054	--	0.1	15.7	47.2	11.0	9.0	5.0	12.0
1105	--	--	7.3	53.2	15.5	8.0	4.0	12.0
Beach Ridges								
944	--	5.0	73.7	20.1	5.7[t]			
1000	0.6	5.5	31.4	46.6	15.9[t]			
1002	0.1	7.5	69.8	19.9	2.7[t]			
1006	0.9	16.7	54.4	27.3	0.7[t]			
1053	18.5	72.0	4.7	0.3	4.5[t]			
1055	0.1	11.3	53.7	21.0	3.0	1.0	3.0	7.0
1104	5.1	68.5	19.1	1.8	0.5[t]	0.5	0.5	4.0
1122	--	13.9	71.2	13.9	1.0[t]			

[t]Total of fines under 63 microns.

ABSTRACT

Lake Rudolf is a non-outlet lake with an area of 7500 sq. km. and a total catchment of 146,000 sq. km. However, about 80-90% of the annual influx appears to be derived from the moist Ethiopian Plateau, via the Omo River with a drainage basin of 73,000 sq. km. In its lower course the Omo is practically an exotic stream, carrying clays, silts and sands obtained primarily from the vertisols and ferrisols of the Ethiopian Plateau. Lake Rudolf fluctuates seasonally with an amplitude of just under 1m, reaching its highest level about 3 months after the late summer discharge maximum of the Omo River.

The Omo Delta is situated in a tectonic depression at the northern end of Lake Rudolf and consists of meander belts, flood basins, delta flats, a now-submerged delta fringe, and a variety of abandoned beach ridges and lake flats. Adjacent to this complex delta plain is Sanderson's gulf, formerly a part of Lake Rudolf extending north to the delta of the Kibish River and now a great mudflat with a playa lake fed mainly by overflow waters from the Omo. The major part of the monograph is devoted to analysis of the geometry, morphology, sediments and soils of the delta plain and their interpretation in terms of changing lake levels, Omo discharge and river profiles. These materials may serve towards a better understanding of the morphology and dynamics of deltas graded to the unstable levels of non-outlet lakes. Also of special interest are the hitherto undescribed giant crack networks characteristic of parts of the Omo delta flats. Finally the modern depositional environments are particularly relevant for interpretation of Pliocene and Pleistocene fossiliferous deposits in the lower Omo Basin.

A large number of historical documents, primarily maps, can be evaluated to trace back the changing delta topography and lake levels until 1888, since which Lake Rudolf has fluctuated within a vertical range of 20m. The lake was 9 or 10m above the 1970 level in 1888 but falling; shortly thereafter it attained a level of +15m during the mid-1890's. Falling rapidly after 1898 the level was only +2.5m in 1908, and after a brief positive oscillation of some 3m in 1917-18, had fallen to -1.5m by the mid-1930's. By 1941 the level was -3.5m, by the mid-1950's -4.5m. Late in 1961 the lake began to rise rapidly and by 1965 had reached its present level. The geomorphologic record extends well back beyond 1888 and, extrapolating from rates of change since that date, it is possible to reconstruct a detailed relative chronology of lake levels and shifting meander trains for at least the preceding 5 centuries. Lake Rudolf was some 25 to 35m higher than today during the first millennium A.D., but then fluctuated between the present level and about

+10m during most of the Medieval period. Beginning at some time between the mid-1500's and mid-1600's, the lake fluctuated between +8 and 15m for about a century, after which the level was quite low until the 1840's, when the level rose rapidly to a high of +15m in the 1870's.

Between 1898 and 1955 the delta shoreline moved 60km, exposing 800 sq. km. of fresh land, while about 200 sq. km. were inundated between 1888 and 1895, and again some 350 sq. km. between 1962 and 1965. Nonetheless, fundamental land use and settlement patterns have remained basically comparable in the intervening 83 years. The possible impacts of the transgression of the late 19th century, the protracted regression after 1898, and the new transgression of the 1960's upon delta land use are discussed. Contemporaneous changes in Omo discharge may also have had economic repercussions for agricultural communities in the meander belts.

The fluctuations of Lake Rudolf since 1888 find many similarities in the ups and downs of other lakes in East Africa, as well as in the discharge records of the Nile system. Study of the available climatic, lake and river records suggests declining rainfall in East Africa south of the equator since the 1870's, and a much more abrupt desiccation north of the equator since 1898. Thereafter climate remained on the dry side, until the 1930's south of 8° S latitude, until the 1960's elsewhere except in central and northern Ethiopia. The abrupt rise of Lake Rudolf after 1961 as well as the equally rapid but ephemeral rise in 1918 were accompanied by an intensification and prolongation of the equinoctial rains over most of East Africa. These regional trends and interrelationships suggest that Lake Rudolf provides a good index of precipitation anomalies in East Africa. The climatic thresholds of 1898 and 1961 were dramatic and the amplitude of corresponding climatic fluctuations is of a scale unrivalled by secular trends of climate in higher latitudes.

BIBLIOGRAPHY

ARAMBOURG, Camille. (1935-1948) Mission scientifique de l'Omo (1932-1933). Géologie-Anthropologie, Muséum National d'Histoire Naturelle, Paris. Fasc. 1 (1935), pp. 1-59; Fasc. 2 (1944), pp. 60-230; Fasc. 3 (1948), pp. 231-562.

ARAMBOURG, Camille; CHAVAILLON, Jean; and COPPENS, Yves. (1969) Résultats de la nouvelle Mission de l'Omo (1968). C. R. Académie des Sciences, Paris, v. D-268:759-62.

ARAMBOURG, Camille, and WOLFF, R. G. (1969) Nouvelles données paléontologiques sur l'age des Turkana Grits à l'ouest du lac Rodolphe. C. R. Sommaire, Société géologique de France, Fasc. 6 (1969), pp. 190-91.

ATHILL, L. F. I. (1920) Through southwestern Abyssinia to the Nile. Geographical Journal, v. 56:347-70.

AUSTIN, H. H. (1899) Journeys to the north of Uganda. II. Lake Rudolf. Geographical Journal, v. 14:148-52.

_____. (1902) A Journey from Omdurman to Mombasa via Lake Rudolf. Geographical Journal, v. 19:669-90.

_____. (1902b) Among swamps and giants in equatorial Africa. London, Pearson, 353pp.

BAGROV, N. A. (1963) On the fluctuations of levels of closed lakes. Soviet Hydrology: selected papers, v. 6:289-94.

BAKER, B. H., and WOHLENBERG, J. (1971) Structure and evolution of the Kenya Rift Valley. Nature, v. 229:538-42.

BEADLE, L. C. (1932a) Observations on the bionomics of some East African swamps. Journal, Linnean Society of London (Zoology), v. 38:135-56.

_____. (1932b) The waters of some East African lakes in relation to their fauna and flora. Journal, Linnean Society of London (Zoology), v. 38:157-211.

BECKINGHAM, C. F., and HUNTINGFORD, G. W. B. (1954) Some records of Ethiopia, 1593-1646. London, Hakluyt Society, 267pp.

BERNARD, H. A., and LeBLANC, R. J. (1965) Resume of the Quaternary geology of the northwestern Gulf of Mexico province. In H. E. WRIGHT and D. G. FREY, The Quaternary of the United States. Princeton, Princeton University Press, pp. 137-85.

BERRY, Leonard, and WHITEMAN, A. J. (1968) The Nile in the Sudan. Geographical Journal, v. 134:1-37.

BISHOP, W. W., and CHAPMAN, G. R. (1970) Early Pliocene sediments and fossils from the northern Kenya Rift valley. Nature, v. 226:914-18.

BISHOP, W. W.; MILLER, J. A.; and FITCH, F. J. (1969) New potassium-argon age determinations relevant to the Miocene fossil mammal sequence in East Africa. American Journal of Science, v. 267:669-99.

BONNEFILLE, Raymonde. (1970) Premiers résultats concernant l'analyse pollinique d'échantillons du Pleistocène inférieur de l'Omo (Éthiopie). C. R. Académie des Sciences, Paris, v. D-270:2430-33.

BONNEFILLE, Raymonde; CHAVAILLON, Jean; and COPPENS, Yves. (1970) Résultats de la nouvelle mission de l'Omo (1969). C. R. Académie des Sciences, Paris, v. D-270:924-27.

BOURG DE BOZAS, Robert de. (1903). D'Addis-Abbaba au Nil par le lac Rodolphe. La Géographie, v. 7:91-112.

BRITISH METEOROLOGICAL OFFICE. (1958) Tables of temperature, relative humidity and precipitation for the world. Part IV: Africa. London, Her Majesty's Stationery Office, 220pp.

BROOKE, J. W. (1905) A journey west and north of Lake Rudolf. Geographical Journal, v. 25:525-31.

BROWN, F. H. (n.d.) Reconnaissance geology of the Nkalabong Range, lower Omo Valley. Unpublished manuscript (1968), 5pp.

BROWN, F. H., and CARMICHAEL, I. S. E. (1969) Quaternary volcanoes of the Lake Rudolf region. I. The Korath Range. Lithos, v. 2:239-60.

BROWN, F. H., and LAJOIE, K. R. (1971) Radiometric age determinations on Pliocene/ Pleistocene formations in the Lower Omo Basin, Ethiopia. Nature, v. 229:483-85.

BUTZER, K. W. (1969) Geological interpretation of two Pleistocene hominid sites in the Lower Omo Basin. Nature, v. 222:1133-35.

_____. (1970) Contemporary depositional environments of the Omo Delta. Nature, v. 226:425-30.

_____. (1971a) The Lower Omo Basin: geology, fauna and hominids of the Plio-Pleistocene formations. Die Naturwissenschaften, v. 58:7-16.

_____. (1971b) Environment and Archeology: an ecological approach to prehistory. Chicago, Aldine, 703pp.

BUTZER, K. W.; BROWN, F. H.; and THURBER, D. L. (1970) Horizontal sediments of the lower Omo Valley: the Kibish Formation. Quaternaria, v. 11(1969):15-30.

BUTZER, K. W., and HANSEN, C. L. (1968) Desert and river in Nubia: geomorphology and prehistoric environments of the Aswan Reservoir. Madison, University of Wisconsin Press, 560pp.

BUTZER, K. W.; ISAAC, G. L.; RICHARDSON, R. L.; and WASHBOURN-KAMAU, C. (n.d.) Quaternary fluctuations of some East African lakes.

BUTZER, K. W., and THURBER, D. L. (1969) Some late Cenozoic sedimentary formations of the Lower Omo Basin. Nature v. 222:1138-43.

178

BULATOVICH, A. K. (1900) Dall'Abissinia al Lago Rodolfo per il Caffa. Bolletino, Società Geografica Italiana, Ser. 4, v. 1:121-42; edited and with an introduction by G. RONCAGLI.

CARR, C. J. (n.d.) A preliminary analysis of the plant ecology of the mesic environments of the Lower Omo River Basin, Ethiopia. Unpublished Field Report, University of Chicago Department of Geography (1970), 73pp.

_____. (n.d.) Ecological studies along the Omo River of Southwest Ethiopia. Unpublished manuscript.

CARTER, D. B. (1954) Climates of Africa and India according to Thornthwaite's 1948 classification. Publications in Climatology, Laboratory of Climatology (Centerton, New Jersey), v. 7, No. 4:449-74.

CAVENDISH, H. S. H. (1898) Through Somaliland and around and south of Lake Rudolf. Geographical Journal, v. 11:372-96.

CERULLI, Ernesta. (1956) Peoples of Southwest Ethiopia and its borderlands (Ethnographic Survey of Africa, Northeast Africa, Part III). London, International African Institute, 148pp.

CHAMPION, A. J. (1937) Physiography of the region to the west and southwest of Lake Rudolf. Geographical Journal, v. 89:97-118.

CHAPPUIS, P. A. (1935) Als Naturforscher in Ostafrika. Stuttgart, Schweizerbartsche, 119pp.

DAINELLI, Giotto. (1943) Geologia dell'Africa orientale. Reale Accademia d'Italia, 3 vol., 464 + 704 + 748pp.

DE HEINZELIN, Jean, and BROWN, F. H. (1970) Some early Pleistocene deposits of the lower Omo Valley: the Usno Beds. Quaternaria, v. 11(1969):31-46.

DE HEINZELIN, Jean; BROWN, F. H.; and HOWELL, F. C. (1971) Pliocene/Pleistocene formations in the Lower Omo Basin, southern Ethiopia. Quaternaria, v. 13(1970), 247-68.

D'HOORE, J. L. (1964) Soil Map of Africa (1:5,000,000). Lagos, FAO, 205pp. and 7 map sheets.

D'OSSAT, G. Angelis, and MILLOSEVICH, F. (1900) Studio geologico sul materiale raccolto da M. Sacchi. Roma, Società Geografica Italiana, 212pp.

DUDAL, R. (ed.). (1965) Dark clay soils of tropical and subtropical regions. Rome, FAO, Agricultural Development Paper 83, 161pp.

ESCHERICH, Georg. (1921) Im Lande des Negus. Berlin, G. Stilke, 2nd ed., 187pp.

FANTOLI, Amilcare. (1965) Contributo alla climatologia dell'Etiopia. Roma, Ministero degli affari esteri, 85 + 558pp.

FISK, H. N. (1952) Geological investigation of the Atchafalaya Basin and the problem of Mississippi River diversion. Vicksburg, Mississippi River Commission, 145pp.

FLOHN, Hermann. (1965) Studies on the meteorology of tropical Africa. Bonner Meteorologische Abhandlungen, v. 5:57pp.

FLOHN, Hermann, and FRAEDRICH, Klaus. (1966) Tagesperiodische Zirkulation und Niederschlagsverteilung am Viktoria-See (Ostafrika). Meteorologische Rundschau, v. 19:157-65.

FUCHS, V. E. (1934) The geological work of the Cambridge Expedition to the East African lakes (1930-31). Part I: Eastern Rift Valley in Kenya Colony. Geological Magazine, v. 71:97-112.

_____. (1935) The Lake Rudolf Rift Valley Expedition (1934). Geographical Journal, v. 86:114-42.

_____. (1939) The geological history of the Lake Rudolf Basin, Kenya Colony. Philosophical Transactions, Royal Society of London, v. 229-B:219-74.

GICHUIYA, S. N. (1971) Easterly disturbances in the south-east monsoon. Proceedings, Symposium on Tropical Meteorology, Honolulu, June 1970. WMO-AMS, in press.

GREER, D. C. (1971) Great Salt Lake, Utah. Map Supplement 14, Annals, Association of American Geographers, v. 61.

GROVE, A. T., and GOUDIE, A. S. (1971) Secrets of Lake Stefanie's past. Geographical Magazine, v. 43:542-47.

GULLIVER, P., and GULLIVER, P. H. (1953) The Central Nilo-Hamites (Ethnographic Survey of Africa, East Central Africa, Part VII). London, International African Institute, 106pp.

GWYNN, C. W. (1911) A journey in southern Abyssinia. Geographical Journal, v. 38: 113-39.

GWYNNE, M. D. (1969) The South Turkana Expedition. I. Preliminary report on the 1968 season. Geographical Journal, v. 135:331-42.

HABERLAND, Eike. (1963) Die Galla Süd-Äthiopiens. Stuttgart, Kohlhammer, 815pp. + 92 pl.

HAMMER, R. M. (1971) Spatial characteristics of thunderstorm development in central Sudan. Proceedings Assoc. Amer. Geog., v. 3:67-70.

HARRISON, J. J. (1901) A journey from Zeila to Lake Rudolf. Geographical Journal, v. 18:258-75.

HEDBERG, Olov. (1962) Mountain plants from southern Ethiopia collected by Dr. John Eriksson. Arkiv för Botanik, v. 4:421-35.

HODSON, Arnold. (1929) Journeys from Maji, southwest Abyssinia. Geographical Journal, v. 73:401-28.

HÖHNEL, Ludwig von. (1890) Ostäquatorial-Afrika zwischen Pangani und dem neuentdeckten Rudolf-See. Petermann's Ergänzungsheft, v. 99:44pp.

_____. (1894) Discovery of Lakes Rudolf and Stefanie. London, Longmans, Green, v. 2, 397pp.; trans. by Nancy Bell (Frank Cass Press Reprint, 1968).

_____. (1938) The Lake Rudolf region: its discovery and subsequent exploration, 1888-1909. Journal, Royal African Society of London, v. 37:16-45, 206-26; with a foreword by V. E. FUCHS.

HÖHNEL, Ludwig von; ROSIWAL, A.; TOULA, Franz; and SUESS, Eduard. (1891). Beiträge zur geologischen Kenntniss des östlichen Afrika. Denkschriften, Kaiserliche Akademie der Wissenschaften (Wien), Math-Naturw. Kl., v. 58:140pp.

HOLLAND, W. Pennefather. (1926) Volcanic action north of Rudolf in 1918. Geographical Journal, v. 68:488-91.

HOWELL, F. C. (1968) Omo Research Expedition. Nature, v. 219:567-72.

HUNTINGFORD, G. W. B. (1955) The Galla of Ethiopia. The Kingdoms of Kafa and Janjero (Ethnographic Survey of Africa, Northeastern Africa, II). London, International African Institute, 156pp.

HURST, H. E., and BLACK, R. P. (1963) The Nile Basin. Vol. III, supplement 3. Cairo, Ministry of Public Works, 389pp.

HURST, H. E., and PHILLIPS, P. (1935) The Nile Basin. Vol. III, supplement 1. Cairo, Ministry of Public Works, 567pp.

————. (1939) The Nile Basin. Vol. III, supplement 2. Cairo, 291pp.

JARVIS, C. S. (1936) Flood-stage records of the River Nile. Transactions, American Society of Civil Engineers, v. 101:1012-30.

JEANNEL, René. (1934) Un cimetière d'éléphants. Paris, Société des Amis du Muséum National d'Histoire Naturelle, 159pp.

JENSEN, A. E. (ed.). (1959) Altvölker Süd-Äthiopiens. Stuttgart, Kohlhammer, 600pp.

JOHNSON, D. H. (1962) Rain in East Africa. Quarterly Journal Royal Meteorological Society, v. 88:1-19.

KLEIN, Cippora. (1961) On the fluctuations of the level of the Dead Sea since the beginning of the 19th century. Hydrological Paper, Israel Hydrological Service, v. 7:1-83.

KUBIENA, W. L. (1953) The soils of Europe. London, Murby, 317pp.

KULS, Wolfgang. (1958) Beiträge zur Kulturgeographie der südäthiopischen Seenregion. Frankfurter Geographische Hefte, v. 32:1-179.

LAMB, H. H. (1966) Climate in the 1960's. Geographical Journal, v. 132:183-212.

LEAKEY, R. E. F.; BEHRENSMEYER, A. K.; FITCH, F. J.; MILLER, J. A.; and LEAKEY, M. D. (1970) New hominid remains and early artefacts from northern Kenya. Nature, v. 226:223-30.

LEBON, J. H. G. (1965) Land Use Survey of Sudan (1:1,000,000). World Land Use Survey, Regional Monograph 4, 191pp.

LEONTIEFF, N. de. (1900) Explorations des Provinces équatoriales d'Abissinie. La Géographie, v. 2:105-18.

LEOPOLD, L. B.; WOLMAN, M. G.; and MILLER, J. P. (1964) Fluvial processes in geomorphology. San Francisco, Freeman, 522pp.

LOGAN, W. E. M. (1946) An introduction to the forests of central and southern Ethiopia. Imperial Forestry Institute (Oxford University), Paper 24, pp. 1-58.

MAUD, Philip. (1904) Exploration in the southern borderland of Abyssinia. Geographical Journal, v. 23:552-79.

McCALL, G. J. H.; BAKER, B. H.; and WALSH, John. (1967) Late Tertiary and Quaternary sediments of the Kenya Rift Valley. In W. W. BISHOP and J. D. CLARK (eds.), Background to evolution in Africa. Chicago, University of Chicago Press, pp. 191-220.

MERLA, G. (1963) Missione geologica nell'Etiopia meridionale: notizie geo-morfologiche e geologiche. Giornale di Geologia (Bologna), Ser. 2, v. 31:56pp.

MODHA, M. L. (1967) The ecology of the Nile crocodile on Central Island, Lake Rudolf. East African Wildlife Journal, v. 5:74-95.

MOHR, P. A. (1964) The geology of Ethiopia. Asmara, Univ. Coll. Addis Ababa Press, 286pp.

_____. (1968) The Cainozoic volcanic succession in Ethiopia. Bulletin Volcanologique, v. 32:5-14.

MORISAWA, Marie. (1968) Streams: their dynamics and morphology. New York, McGraw-Hill, 175pp.

MORTH, H. T. (1967) Investigation into the meteorological aspects of the variations in the level of Lake Victoria. Memoirs, East African Meteorological Department, v. 4(2): 1-23.

_____. (1971) A study of the areal and temporal distributions of rainfall anomalies in East Africa. Proceedings, Symposium on Tropical Meteorology, Honolulu, June 1970. WMO-AMS, in press.

NEUMANN, A. H. (1898) Elephant hunting in East Equatorial Africa. London, Rowland Ward, 455pp.

NILE CONTROL STAFF. (1965) The Nile Basin. Vol. III, supplement 6. Cairo, Ministry of Public Works, 427pp.

NOWACK, Ernst. (1954) Land und Volk der Konso. Bonner Geographische Abhandlungen, v. 14:1-71.

OLIVER, Roland, and MATHEW, Gervase (eds.). (1966) History of East Africa. Oxford, Clarendon Press, v. 1, 500pp.

OSMAN, O. E., and HASTENRATH, S. L. (1969) On the synoptic climatology of summer rainfall over Central Sudan. Archiv für Meteorologie, Geophysik und Bioklimatologie, Ser. B, v. 17:297-324.

PARKER, G. G. (1964) Piping, a geomorphic agent in landform development of the drylands. International Association of Scientific Hydrology, Report 65 (Berkeley), pp. 103-13.

PATTERSON, Bryan. (1966) A new locality for early Pleistocene fossils in north-western Kenya. Nature, v. 212:577-79.

PATTERSON, Bryan; BEHRENSMEYER, A. K.; and SILL, W.D. (1970) Geology and fauna of a new Pliocene locality in northwestern Kenya. Nature, v. 226:918-21.

PATTERSON, Bryan, and HOWELLS, W. W. (1967) Hominid humeral fragment from early Pleistocene of northwestern Kenya. Science, v. 156:64-66.

PAULI, Elisabeth. (1950) Die Splitterstämme nördlich des Rudolfsees. Annali Laterani (Vatican City), v. 14:61-191.

PAYNE, T. G. (1942) Stratigraphical analysis and environmental reconstruction. Bulletin, Amer. Assoc. Petrol. Geol., v. 26:1697-1770.

PICCHI-SERMOLLI, R. E. G. (1953) Tropical East Africa. In Plant ecology: reviews of research. Arid Zone Research (UNESCO), v. 6:302-60.

_____. (1957) Una Carta geobotanica dell'Africa orientale. Webbia, Raccolta di Scritti botanici (Firenze), v. 13, part 1:15-132.

PIKE, J. G. (1965) The sunspot/lake level relationship and the control of Lake Nyasa. Journal, Institute of Water Engineers, v. 19:221-26.

REILLY, T. A.; MUSSET, A. E.; RAJA, P. R. S.; GRASTY, R. L.; and WALSH, J. (1966) Age and polarity of the Turkana lavas, northwest Kenya. Nature, v. 210: 1145-46.

RHEMTULLA, Sultan. (1970) The South Turkana Expedition. III. A geological reconnaissance of South Turkana. Geographical Journal, v. 136:61-73.

RICHARDS, C. G. (ed.). (1961) Some historic journeys in East Africa. London, Oxford Univ. Press, 134pp.

RIEHL, Herbert. (1954) Tropical meteorology. New York, McGraw Hill, 392pp.

ROBBINS, L. H. (n.d.) The archaeology of the Turkana district. In preparation.

ROGER, Jean. (1944) Mollusques fossiles et subfossiles du Bassin du lac Rodolphe. In: C. ARAMBOURG, 1944, pp. 119-55.

RUDLOFF, H. von. (1967) Die Schwankungen und Pendelungen des Klimas in Europa seit dem Beginn der regelmässigen Instrumentenbeobachtungen (1960). Brunswick, Vieweg (Die Wissenschaft, vol. 122), 370pp.

SAGGERSON, E. P., and BAKER, B. H. (1965) Post-Jurassic erosion-surfaces in eastern Kenya and their deformation in relation to rift structure. Quarterly Journal, Geological Society of London, v. 121:51-72.

SAINT-ARROMAN, R. de (ed.). (1906) De la Mer Rouge à l'Atlantique à travers l'Afrique tropicale (Mission Scientifique du Bourg de Bozas). Paris, Rudeval, 442pp.

SCHATTNER, Isaac. (1962) The Lower Jordan Valley: a study in the fluviomorphology of an arid region. Scripta Hierosolymitana, v. 12:1-123.

SCHOKALSKAJA, S. J. (1953) Die Böden Afrikas. Berlin, Akademie Verlag, 408pp.

SCHOTTENLOHER, Rudolf. (1938) Bericht über eine Forschungsreise in Südäthiopien. Sitzungsberichte, math.-naturw. Abteilung, Bayerische Akademie der Wissenschaften (Munich), pp. 205-10.

SCHUMM, S. A. (1963) Sinuosity of alluvial rivers of the Great Plains. Bulletin, Geological Society of America, v. 74:1089-1100.

183

SCOTT, Hugh. (1952) Journey to the Gughé Highlands (Southern Ethiopia), 1948-49. Proceedings, Linnean Society of London, v. 163:85-189.

SEMMEL, Arno. (1964) Beitrag zur Kenntnis einiger Böden des Hochlandes von Godjam (Äthiopien). Monatshefte, Neues Jahrbuch für Geologie und Palaontologie, v. 8: 474-87.

SMITH, A. D. (1896) Expedition through Somaliland to Lake Rudolf. Geographical Journal, v. 8:221-39.

_____. (1897) Through unknown African countries. London, Arnold, 471pp. (Greenwood Press Reprint, 1969).

_____. (1900) An expedition between Lake Rudolf and the Nile. Geographical Journal, v. 16:600-625.

SMITH, G. D., and others. (1960) Soil Classification, a comprehensive system (7th Approximation). Washington, U.S. Department of Agriculture, 265pp.

STIGAND, C. H. (1910) To Abyssinia through an unknown land. Philadelphia, Lippincott, 352pp.

SUZUKI, Hideo. (1967) Some aspects of Ethiopian climates. Ethiopian Geographical Journal, v. 5(2):19-24.

TATO, Kebede. (1964) Rainfall in Ethiopia. Ethiopian Geographical Journal, v. 2(2):28-36.

TEMPLE, P. H. (1968) Further observations on the glaciers of the Ruwenzori. Geografiska Annaler, v. 50A:136-61.

THOMPSON, B. W. (1965) The climate of Africa. London, Oxford University Press, 132 pl.

THORNTHWAITE, C. W., and MATHER, J. C. (1955) The Water Balance. Publications in Climatology, Laboratory of Climatology (Centerton, New Jersey), v. 8, No. 1: 104pp.

TOTHILL, J. D. (1946) The origins of the Sudan Gezira clay plain. Sudan Notes and Records, v. 27:153-83.

TREWARTHA, G. T. (1961) The Earth's problem climates. Madison, University of Wisconsin Press, 334pp.

TUCKER, A. N., and BRYAN, M. A. (1956) The non-Bantu languages of northeastern Africa (Handbook of African Languages, Part III). London, International African Institute, 228pp.

UNESCO. (1958) Vegetation map of Africa south of the Tropic of Cancer (1:10 million). Paris, Unesco.

U.S. DEPARTMENT OF COMMERCE. (1959) World Weather Records 1941-50. Washington, 1361pp.

_____. (1967) World Weather Records 1951-60. Washington, 545pp.

184

U.S. WEATHER BUREAU. (1965-70) Synoptic Weather Maps (Daily Series). Northern hemisphere Sea Level and 500 Millibar Charts. Washington, monthly books for 1960 through 1964.

VANNUTELLI, Lamberto, and CITERNI, Carlo. (1897) Relazione preliminare sui risultati geografici della seconda spedizione Bòttego. Bolletino, Società Geografica Italiana, Ser. 3, v. 10:320-30.

_____. (1899) L'Omo: Viaggio di esplorazione nell'Africa Orientale. Milano, U. Hoepli, 650pp.

WALSH, John, and DODSON, R. G. (1969) Geology of Northern Turkana. Mines and Geological Department of Kenya, Rept. 82, 42pp. and 1:500,000 map.

WEICKMANN, Ludwig, Jr. (1963) Mittlere Luftdruckverteilung im Meeresniveau während der Hauptjahreszeiten im Bereiche um Afrika, in dem Indischen Ozean und den angrenzenden Teilen Asiens. Meteorologische Rundschau, v. 16:89-100.

_____. (1964) Mittlere Lage und vertikale Struktur grossräumiger Diskontinuitäten im Luftdruck- und Strömungsfeld der Tropenzone zwischen Afrika und Indonesien. Meteorologische Rundschau, v. 17:105-12.

WELLBY, M. S. (1900) King Menelik's dominions and the country between Lake Gallop (Rudolf) and the Nile Valley. Geographical Journal, v. 16:292-306.

WHITWORTH, T. (1965) The Pleistocene lake beds of Kabua, northern Kenya. Durham University Journal, v. 57:88-100.

WORTHINGTON, E. B. (1932) The lakes of Kenya and Uganda. Geographical Journal, v. 79:275-97.

WORTHINGTON, E. B., and RICARDO, C. K. (1935) The fish of Lake Rudolf and Lake Baringo. Journal, Linnean Society of London (Zoology), v. 39:353-89.

ZAVATTARI, Edoardo. (1941) Vom Djuba-Fluss zum Rodolfsee: geographisch-biologische Reisen und Entdeckungen im südlichen Äthiopien. Mitteilungen, Geographische Gesellschaft Wien, v. 84:86-118.

_____. (1942) La risoluzione del problema del lago Stefania. Bolletino, Società Geografica Italiana, Ser. 7, v. 7:321-44.

THE UNIVERSITY OF CHICAGO
DEPARTMENT OF GEOGRAPHY
RESEARCH PAPERS (Lithographed, 6×9 Inches)

(Available from Department of Geography, 5828 S. University Ave., The University of Chicago, Chicago, Illinois 60637. Price: $4.50 each; by series subscription, $4.00 each.)

* Out of print.

*45. ZADROZNY, MITCHELL G. *Water Utilization in the Middle Mississippi Valley*

*46. AHMED, G. MUNIR. *Manufacturing Structure and Pattern of Waukegan–North Chicago*

*47. RANDALL, DARRELL. *Factors of Economic Development and the Okovango Delta*

48. BOXER, BARUCH. *Israeli Shipping and Foreign Trade* 1957. 176 pp.

*49. MAYER, HAROLD M. *The Port of Chicago and the St. Lawrence Seaway*

*50. PATTISON, WILLIAM D. *Beginnings of the American Rectangular Land Survey System, 1784–1800* 1957. 2d printing 1963. 260 pp. Available from Ohio Historical Society.

*51. BROWN, ROBERT HAROLD. *Political Areal-Functional Organization: With Special Reference to St. Cloud, Minnesota.*

*52. BEYER, JACQUELYN. *Integration of Grazing and Crop Agriculture: Resources Management Problems in the Uncompahgre Valley Irrigation Project.*

53. ACKERMAN, EDWARD A. *Geography as a Fundamental Research Discipline* 1958. 40 pp. $1.00

*54. AL-KHASHAB, WAFIQ HUSSAIN. *The Water Budget of the Tigris and Euphrates Basin*

*55. LARIMORE, ANN EVANS. *The Alien Town: Patterns of Settlement in Busoga, Uganda*

56. MURPHY, FRANCIS C. *Regulating Flood-Plain Development* 1958. 216 pp.

*57. WHITE, GILBERT F., et al. *Changes in Urban Occupance of Flood Plains in the United States*

*58. COLBY, MARY MC RAE. *The Geographic Structure of Southeastern North Carolina*

*59. MEGEE, MARY CATHERINE. *Monterrey, Mexico: Internal Patterns and External Relations*

60. WEBER, DICKINSON. *A Comparison of Two Oil City Business Centers (Odessa-Midland, Texas)* 1958. 256 pp.

61. PLATT, ROBERT S. *Field Study in American Geography* 1959. 408 pp.

62. GINSBURG, NORTON, editor. *Essays on Geography and Economic Development* 1960. 196 pp.

*63. HARRIS, CHAUNCY D., and FELLMANN, JEROME D. *International List of Geographical Serials* (See 138)

*64. TAAFFE, ROBERT N. *Rail Transportation and the Economic Development of Soviet Central Asia*

*65. SHEAFFER, JOHN R. *Flood Proofing: An Element in a Flood Damage Reduction Program*

*66. RODGERS, ALLAN L. *The Industrial Geography of the Port of Genova*

*67. KENYON, JAMES B. *Industrial Localization and Metropolitan Growth: The Paterson-Passaic District.*

68. GINSBURG, NORTON. *An Atlas of Economic Development* 1961. 119 pp. 14×8½". Cloth. University of Chicago Press.

69. CHURCH, MARTHA. *Spatial Organization of Electric Power Territories in Massachusetts* 1960. 200 pp.

70. WHITE, GILBERT F., et al. *Papers on Flood Problems* 1961. 234 pp.

71. GILBERT, E. W. *The University Town in England and West Germany* 1961. 79 pp. 4 plates. 30 maps and diagrams.

72. BOXER, BARUCH. *Ocean Shipping in the Evolution of Hong Kong* 1961. 108 pp.

*73. ROBINSON, IRA M. *New Industrial Towns of Canada's Resource Frontier* (Research Paper No. 4, Program of Education and Research in Planning, The University of Chicago.)

74. TROTTER, JOHN E. *State Park System in Illinois* 1962. 152 pp.

*75. BURTON, IAN. *Types of Agricultural Occupance of Flood Plains in the United States*

*76. PRED, ALLAN. *The External Relations of Cities during 'Industrial Revolution'*

77. BARROWS, HARLAN H. *Lectures on the Historical Geography of the United States as Given in 1933* Edited by WILLIAM A. KOELSCH. 1962. 248 pp.

*78. KATES, ROBERT WILLIAM. *Hazard and Choice Perception in Flood Plain Management*

79. HUDSON, JAMES. *Irrigation Water Use in the Utah Valley, Utah* 1962. 249 pp.

*80. ZELINSKY, WILBUR. *A Bibliographic Guide to Population Geography*

*81. DRAINE, EDWIN H. *Import Traffic of Chicago and Its Hinterland*

*82. KOLARS, JOHN F. *Tradition, Season, and Change in a Turkish Village* NAS-NRC Foreign Field Research Program Report No. 15.

*83. WIKKRAMATILEKE, RUDOLPH. *Southeast Ceylon: Trends and Problems in Agricultural Settlement*

84. KANSKY, K. J. *Structure of Transportation Networks: Relationships between Network Geometry and Regional Characteristics* 1963. 155 pp.

*85. BERRY, BRIAN J. L. *Commercial Structure and Commercial Blight*

86. BERRY, BRIAN J. L., and TENNANT, ROBERT J. *Chicago Commercial Reference Handbook* 1963. 278 pp.

*87. BERRY, BRIAN J. L., and HANKINS, THOMAS D. *A Bibliographic Guide to the Economic Regions of the United States*

*88. MARCUS, MELVIN G. *Climate-Glacier Studies in the Juneau Ice Field Region, Alaska*

*89. SMOLE, WILLIAM J. *Owner-Cultivatorship in Middle Chile*

*90. HELVIG, MAGNE. *Chicago's External Truck Movements: Spatial Interaction between the Chicago Area and Its Hinterland*

* Out of print.

91. HILL, A. DAVID. *The Changing Landscape of a Mexican Municipio, Villa Las Rosas, Chiapas* NAS-NRC Foreign Field Research Program Report No. 26. 1964. 121 pp.
92. SIMMONS, JAMES W. *The Changing Pattern of Retail Location* 1964. 202 pp.
*93. WHITE, GILBERT F. *Choice of Adjustment to Floods*
94. MCMANIS, DOUGLAS R. *The Initial Evaluation and Utilization of the Illinois Prairies, 1815–1840* 1964. 109 pp.
*95. PERLE, EUGENE D. *The Demand for Transportation: Regional and Commodity Studies in the United States*
*96. HARRIS, CHAUNCY D. *Annotated World List of Selected Current Geographical Serials in English*
97. BOWDEN, LEONARD W. *Diffusion of the Decision To Irrigate: Simulation of the Spread of a New Resource Management Practice in the Colorado Northern High Plains* 1965. 146 pp.
98. KATES, ROBERT W. *Industrial Flood Losses: Damage Estimation in the Lehigh Valley* 1965. 76 pp.
*99. RODER, WOLF. *The Sabi Valley Irrigation Projects*
100. SEWELL, W. R. DERRICK. *Water Management and Floods in the Fraser River Basin* 1965. 163 pp.
*101. RAY, D. MICHAEL. *Market Potential and Economic Shadow: A Quantitative Analysis of Industrial Location in Southern Ontario*
102. AHMAD, QAZI. *Indian Cities: Characteristics and Correlates* 1965. 184 pp.
103. BARNUM, H. GARDINER. *Market Centers and Hinterlands in Baden-Württemberg* 1966. 172 pp.
104. SIMMONS, JAMES W. *Toronto's Changing Retail Complex* 1966. 126 pp.
105. SEWELL, W. R. DERRICK, et al. *Human Dimensions of Weather Modification* 1966. 423 pp.
106. SAARINEN, THOMAS FREDERICK. *Perception of the Drought Hazard on the Great Plains* 1966. 183 pp.
107. SOLZMAN, DAVID M. *Waterway Industrial Sites: A Chicago Case Study* 1967. 138 pp.
108. KASPERSON, ROGER E. *The Dodecanese: Diversity and Unity in Island Politics* 1967. 184 pp.
109. LOWENTHAL, DAVID, editor. *Environmental Perception and Behavior* 1967. 88 pp.
110. REED, WALLACE E. *Areal Interaction in India: Commodity Flows of the Bengal-Bihar Industrial Area* 1967. 210 pp.
*111. BERRY, BRIAN J. L. *Essays on Commodity Flows and the Spatial Structure of the Indian Economy*
112. BOURNE, LARRY S. *Private Redevelopment of the Central City: Spatial Processes of Structural Change in the City of Toronto* 1967. 199 pp.
113. BRUSH, JOHN E., and GAUTHIER, HOWARD L., JR. *Service Centers and Consumer Trips: Studies on the Philadelphia Metropolitan Fringe* 1968. 182 pp.
114. CLARKSON, JAMES D. *The Cultural Ecology of a Chinese Village, Cameron Highlands, Malaysia* 1968. 174 pp.
115. BURTON, IAN, KATES, ROBERT W., and SNEAD, RODMAN E. *The Human Ecology of Coastal Flood Hazard in Megalopolis* 1968. 196 pp.
*116. MURDIE, ROBERT, *Factorial Ecology of Metropolitan Toronto, 1951–1961*
117. WONG, SHUE TUCK. *Perception of Choice and Factors Affecting Industrial Water Supply Decisions in Northeastern Illinois* 1968. 96 pp.
118. JOHNSON, DOUGLAS. *The Nature of Nomadism: A Comparative Study of Pastoral Migrations in Southwestern Asia and Northern Africa* 1969. 200 pp.
119. DIENES, LESLIE. *Locational Factors and Locational Developments in the Soviet Chemical Industry* 1969. 285 pp.
120. MIHELIC, DUSAN. *The Political Element in the Port Geography of Trieste* 1969. 104 pp.
121. BAUMANN, DUANE. *The Recreational Use of Domestic Water Supply Reservoir: Perception and Choice* 1969. 125 pp.
122. LIND, AULIS O. *Coastal Landforms of Cat Island, Bahamas: A Study of Holocene Accretionary Topography and Sea-Level Change* 1969. 156 pp.
123. WHITNEY, JOSEPH. *China: Area, Administration and Nation Building* 1970. 198 pp.
124. EARICKSON, ROBERT. *The Spatial Behavior of Hospital Patients: A Behavioral Approach to Spatial Interaction in Metropolitan Chicago* 1970. 198 pp.
125. DAY, JOHN CHADWICK. *Managing the Lower Rio Grande: An Experience in International River Development* 1970. 277 pp.
126. MAC IVER, IAN. *Urban Water Supply Alternatives: Perception and Choice in the Grand Basin Ontario* 1970. 178 pp.
127. GOHEEN, PETER G. *Victorian Toronto, 1850 to 1900: Pattern and Process of Growth* 1970. 278 pp
128. GOOD, CHARLES M. *Rural Markets and Trade in East Africa* 1970. 252 pp.
129. MEYER, DAVID R. *Spatial Variation of Black Urban Households* 1970. 127 pp.
130. GLADFELTER, BRUCE G. *Meseta and Campiña Landforms in Central Spain* 1971. 204 pp.
131. NEILS, ELAINE M. *Reservation to City: Indian Urbanization and Federal Relocation* 1971. 200 pp.
132. MOLINE, NORMAN T. *Mobility and the Small Town, 1900–1930* 1971. 169 pp.

* Out of print.

133. SCHWIND, PAUL J. *Migration and Regional Development in the United States* 1971. 170 pp.

134. PYLE, GERALD F. *Heart Disease, Cancer and Stroke in Chicago* 1971. 292 pp.

135. JOHNSON, JAMES. F. *Renovated Waste Water* 1971. 155 pp.

136. BUTZER, KARL W. *Recent History of an Ethiopian Delta* 1971.

137. HARRIS, CHAUNCY D. *Annotated World List of Selected Current Geographical Serials in English, French, and German* 3rd edition 1971. 77 pp.

138. HARRIS, CHAUNCY D., and FELLMANN, JEROME D. *International List of Geographical Serials.* 2nd edition 1971. 267 pp.